P9-EDU-363

VOYAGE
TO THE
OTHER EXTREME

MARILÚ MALLET

VOYAGE TO THE OTHER EXTREME

FIVE STORIES

TRANSLATED FROM THE SPANISH

BY ALAN BROWN

MONTREAL

Translated and published with the assistance of the Canada Council.

Book design by Simon Dardick.
Photograph of the author by Guy Borremans.
Typeset in Goudy Old Style by Zibra Inc.
Printed by Les Éditions Marquis Ltée.

Dépôt légal, Bibliothèque Nationale du Québec
and the National Library of Canada, 4th trimester, 1985.

Canadian Cataloguing in Publication Data

Mallet, Marilú
[Les compagnons de l'horloge-pointeuse. English]
Voyage to the other extreme
Translation of : Les compagnons de l'horloge-pointeuse.
ISBN 0-919890-62-8
I. Title. II. Title: Les compagnons de l'horloge-pointeuse.
English.
PS8576.A5336C6513 1986 C843'.54 C85-090295-9
PR9199.3.M34C6513 1986

Véhicule Press, P.O.B. 125, Place du Parc Station,
Montréal, Québec, Canada H2W 2M9

Printed in Canada

CONTENTS

The Loyal Order of the Time-Clock

I KNOW I'm fat and boring. I realize it when I get to the office and, without even thinking about it, start tapping with my shoe at the loose piece in the parquet flooring. I've had this little habit for ten years now, ever since we moved here to the central building on the Alameda. I never know what to do all day long. Not that I lack imagination; but there's a certain absence of desire to be up and about. There are times when I'd like to move my desk, or stop saying hello to the others. I don't dare. Something could happen! What I admire most about Don Julian is the way he keeps busy. Don Julian is my boss. This is the timekeeper's office. My job is to wait until everybody has punched in, pick up the cards and calculate the late arrivals.

In the mornings I check the previous day's overtime. But the Ministry doesn't pay for overtime. My boss is very hard-working. He's always fitting glass into little metal tubes, very strange, though of course I know by now that he's making telescopes. Because he gradually brought in his emery wheel and other tools. He has a big brown table covered with pliers, tweezers and screws, and nobody bats an eye at the fact that he assembles telescopes in the office. Or that he only uses the phone for his private business. Or that people come to see him, and the little sofa is always full of customers, what with the acrylic sign outside that says: "Telescopes made here." I watch him for hours on end, the patient way he manages to place a tiny screw with his tweezers. One of my tasks is answering the phone and it's almost always for him, about his work, for he makes new telescopes as people order them. Or else it's the dwarfs calling. Don Julian is a skinny, nervous man. His wife is like him, very skinny. They've been married twenty years. The first son they had was a dwarf. The second son they had was a dwarf. The third one was normal. The fourth child turned out to be yet another dwarf. Sometimes I wonder if they adopted them. I admire his patience. When I watch him I get the urge to marry or move my desk, but the only thing that happens is that I've reached the second section of the paper and my leg is moving, making my foot tap on the loose piece of flooring. I read the paper from beginning to end, I don't even skip the obituaries. It's entertaining, but not very. The truth is, I'm always bored, it must be from living alone. Though I was lucky to find this boarding-house, not far from here. They don't serve breakfast, but what do you want for the price? And the house is quake-proof, after all. That's the main thing: quake-proof and hot running water.

"Azucenas! How's the old fatso?"

Guzman and I always trade newspapers. He buys El Clarin, I buy El Mercurio, and we make the first trade at ten in the morning, then again at eleven with other colleagues. Of course, it's always the same news. At one o'clock we leave for lunch, and walk all together down Bandera Street to the

Mapocho River district. I always go back to the office early. Don Julian doesn't go out. He brings a box lunch or one of the dwarfs comes with a hot dish. He's always fiddling with some little bolt that he can't screw in. In the afternoons his customers arrive and fill the office.

Today I came across a surprising news item. I talked about it over lunch with Guzman in the Frying Fish: incredible that such a thing can happen in Chile in the twentieth century. Those poor people! And so far away! Perhaps near C——. A little later I bought a map and we realized it was near Serena in the interior. Even farther inland than where Doña Gabriela Mistral was born, much farther, right in the mountains. I tried to show it to Don Julian, but he was quite taken up toying with a miniscule nut. Guzman called me on the intercom saying bring the map, and there we were looking, with the people from room seven fourteen, seeing where the flood was. Everybody talked a lot, especially Lucy Varela and the other secretary. Those two are always organizing meetings or demonstrations or God knows what. They say we mustn't just sit on our thumbs. I was rather impetuous. That's what I think now. Then I had the urge to do something different, something that . . . something just to show them. So I offered to get a collection going, though I'm not a great talker, I did the seventh floor and then the sixth, with my newspaper, explaining. And you should have seen what they brought! I can't even cram the stuff into my closet! I collected ten kilos of lentils, five kilos of string beans and twenty bags of powdered milk. And three cartons of old clothes. The boss was giving me dirty looks, but I went collecting on the lower floors just the same. A colleague said I should go to another Ministry to rustle up help.

Now we're into the third day of this affair and we've had to evacuate the office to make room for parcels.

"But what can I do, Don Julian!"

He doesn't know what to do with his customers. The smallest dwarfs take up position in the doorway to serve them. But what a disaster! Twenty days with nothing to eat and flooded out of house and home! It's enough to make you feel a little solidarity with others, eh?

"Can't you see we have to do something to emerge from our underdevelopment, Don Julian?" The demagogue was coming out in me.

Guzman and I went to the Ministry of Education. They're going to send along a ballet troupe and a film when we deliver the packets. Now that's what I call assistance!

"Good old Fatso Azucenas! He's given up clock-watching!" people say to me. I never noticed before that people didn't like punching in.

The Defence Department is giving blankets, and we'll travel in their trucks. Who'd have thought it? And all I did was go around with the newspaper story. Sure, sure, I did a bit of talking, too. I know my sales pitch by heart now. And I've lost weight, that's worthwhile in itself. We're going to end the collection on Friday the 13th, not because we want to but because the Undersecretary came along and said our motivation was good but everything was piling up in the offices. It's true, government employees are hanging around in the corridors, doing nothing but talk. Others take off downtown on personal errands. There are cardboard boxes everywhere, clothing, shoes, food, in the rooms, the toilets, the corridors, on the chairs, the desks, in the closets. I don't know why they all ask my permission, as if I were the boss. Oh, yes, I'm still in charge of the timekeeping records. But I've almost forgotten that, I seem to be in another world.

We're leaving Saturday for the village of C——, in three trucks, plus a bus for the ballet troupe.

"Very well, Don Julian. I'm asking for my days off, but you should understand that I'm not going to leave a task like this to just anybody, it's a great responsibility, and letting them go by themselves is no solution, either! It's as if you handed out unassembled telescopes to your customers.!"

At last he began to understand. And off I went with Guzman for C——. Luckily I ended up in the truck with the nurses. Liliana and Gladys. And Corporal Fuenzalidas at the wheel. I'm crammed against the right-hand door, you'd have to see it to believe it: they're like me, plump as pudding, those two girls! Just my type! They work in the National Health Service and are coming along to care for the sick. The newspaper said there were people injured, and quite a few. The time goes by quickly what with talking, and anyway we had an early start at seven. The place is near Serena, in the interior. The truck follows the curves, this way and that way, and there's always a leg against mine. Gladys, she said I could call her. She gives me lots of little smiles. Is this me, Guzman? I never had any luck with women, now I have to make a pass. The fact is, I'm shy. We had to tank up on gas and the Corporal got out with Liliana. Gladys and I, we stayed in the cab alone. She sort of snuggled up to me and I had to put my arm around her shoulders, very affectionate, as they tell it in the Ministry, and without intending to I touched one of her breasts. It's soft, I thought. And she looked at me with her little smile. Just then the others arrived. They asked:

"What's going on?"

"Funny business," said Gladys.

"Don't get any ideas," I warned them.

She told me she lived in Santa Rosa near Matta Avenue.

She's separated and has a little boy. They talked about the Health Service, how hard they work, and . . . there we were in Los Vilos, time for lunch. We had seafood and white wine and got pretty happy. I started telling jokes, a thing I never do. I hear lots of them, of course, at work. We talked about my job, and about the luck of the road, for we saw a man in a loose black overcoat, with a black cat, and I'm superstitious. It happened again somewhere near Tongoi. Seeing him twice gave me the creeps. Shortly after we stopped for a Pilsener and everybody had something to say about the incident. So we were getting close to Serena, then going by the place where the famous Gabriela Mistral had lived. You should have seen me . . . I wasn't shy anymore, and I sat between the two of them, my arms around their shoulders, and giving them a pinch from time to time. What tremendous legs, Guzman! (But where did you get to? There wasn't a sign of you anywhere!) And this was me, who'd always felt fat and boring!

We were approaching C——, up in the mountains already. What a surprise! There wasn't a soul in the place. And no flood! After some effort we did find an old man. He said they all went out in the fields, and came back just before dark.

"All of them?"

"Well . . . the people . . . " he replied.

It was a strange place. There was no village square, there were no trees, just a general store on one corner, and the main street. We got out, and so did the ballet and movie people. Liliana said it was all the fault of the black cat and the man in the loose overcoat. That evening the villagers came back from the fields and stared at us, astounded. The little old guy we'd spoken to played the trumpet. And — what a scare! — there was the man in the loose overcoat, parading in front of the public with his cat on his shoulders and a violin. It's like a tale of the possessed, I thought. I started out by making a speech about the flood and the disasters that take place in Chile. I had it all ready, and even though there was no flood I had to say something. The people watched us suspiciously. The worst thing was when we showed the movie — it was a nice film, for my taste — the people left and the children ran away crying. The ballet troupe danced to pacify them. Then the people barbecued some young llamas, fit to make you lick your fingers. And we handed out the relief packages, the blankets, the food, everything. The old clothes, too. The keeper of the general store got angry. He said we were going to put him out of business. But the village people were ever so pleased. They came, and they kept coming, you had no idea where they came from, maybe from up on the mountain. Or maybe I just imagined them all, we drank so much pisco, even Corporal Fuenzalida, who fell asleep. I went off for a little chat with Gladys near a gateway where there were some bushes . . . . Did we have a nice time! Wow! We were almost caught by an old woman who came poking around there. Guzman was chatting with Liliana. Somebody allotted a ballerina for Corporal Fuenzalida to chase. The people started singing and dancing the cueca. Gladys and I, by the gate in the bushes, went on with what we were doing and so forth. Suddenly the man in the overcoat appeared, playing the violin as he came.

"Gladys, we'd better stop!" I whispered, and jumped to my feet.

I walked over to where everybody was and started talking about the quality of the meat. I have no idea why I got to talking about white flesh . . . I'm so shy! Then a group of peasants told me they had a present for us. A thank-you gift for the Ministry. How original, eh Guzman? Nothing more nor less than a llama! A llama with a leash just like a dog.

We spent the night in the village. I stayed at Peyuco's house, the owner of the llama. So nothing doing with Gladys. But nothing. The girls slept in the school. Next day, for lunch:

"Hey! Chicken stew with dried corn!"

We drove back. I don't know what was up with Gladys, she was playing hard to get. I rubbed my leg on hers and she moved it away. I tried it out on Liliana. Mind you, the animal didn't make things any easier. Lying with his four legs tied up at our feet. But he could move! He was a real agitator, Lord knows! He made as much fuss as two hens. I took this as my excuse to calm the girls with gentle pats, incidentally stroking Gladys' knees, but nothing doing. I slid my hand up a little further. Then she laughed the way she had before. She gave me her phone number. We agreed to get together in Santiago. I'll call her up at the Health Service. The return trip was fast. The Corporal didn't say a word all the way. Except for grumbling about a waste of time, as he called it, adding that more important things were cooking in the capital. On Tuesday at the Ministry they nearly died, they were so impressed when I walked in with the llama. Don Julian was mad because I put it in the office. Later when it filled up with his customers they all wanted to see the animal up close. One of the dwarfs began charging admission. He explained that it was to buy sweets. These kids! My boss's boss called me up:

"You can't keep that critter in the office!"

"I can't take it to my boarding-house," I said.

I went off to the zoo, intending to donate it. They liked the idea.

"But you'll have to get a gift certification from the owner."

"The owner presented it to the Ministry and the Ministry doesn't want it," I said.

I went back to the office and brought my boss's boss up to date. He wrote the certificate for me. What with all this fuss I couldn't even call Gladys, especially because the llama chewed my pocket and ate her number . . . . And imagine my surprise when the Inspector General's people brought me a summons because I had donated an object before it was entered on inventory.

"That's not my fault!" I shouted.

One sure thing is, I don't eat lunch at the Frying Fish with Guzman any more. A poor guy just trying to do something for his country . . . no lunch for me. They say I'm still losing weight. It's ten days now since the animal arrived. The office is filthy. I clean it with loving care. The poor creature spits occasionally.

"Don't worry, you'll be going to the zoo," I console him softly.

Maybe I should listen to them. They said I was summoned. It was the people in Seven Fourteen:

"Go to the Inspector General's office and ask for Don Crispin, in 'Disciplinary Measures.' "

I went, and there was no charge against me at all. It was a joke. I came back to the office about two in the afternoon and found no one there. Suddenly I heard noise and singing coming from the reception hall. I went to have a look at what was going on. There was a big laugh when I walked in. They were eating the llama. It's the old story: they resent me because of the time-cards. One man tripped me up in the doorway:

"Just wait, you son of a whore, now you're going to get my docked time right up the ass."

I left for home. On the way I met Pepe Lazo. After all these years! He comes from Chillan, just like me. He wants us to go into business together. Paper Christmas trees. We had a coffee and a chat and afterwards we went to his room. He showed me the little trees. There's nothing to it! You wrap some cellophane around the sticks and that's it! This is a good deal!

So now I'm doing the same as Don Julian. I stamp the cards and then get down to manufacturing the merchandise. A little money on the side. I bought a new suit at Falabella's. Living is so expensive. Lucy Varela and the other secretary are going around collecting gold rings for the reconstruction of the nation.

"Those two switched sides fast, eh Don Julian?"

He doesn't even answer. He's all wrapped up trying to get some little screw in its hole. People are telling all kinds of stories. Employees being arrested. Others getting fired. Many talk about torture . . . . Me, I don't pick a fight with anybody. I just look after the customers who phone. I don't even think about Gladys, or the llama, or things like helping people. I don't even read the paper. I drift with the times, that's all. Yes, I drift, and I spend the whole day making little Christmas trees to sell in December.

Blind Alley

A STRANGE coincidence: the country's Cultural Ministry was located in a cul-de-sac. Not that I think blind alleys are sinister or anything. Our alley, for example, was famous. Not for its cultural activities but for its well-known brothels. Big old homes, formerly upper class, converted now into quick-trick accommodations. Where you could find any kind of room, from the fashionable colonial style to one with a Hindu or Japanese décor. The price included a private bathroom and a whore with varicose veins. What more could a civil servant ask, right in the middle of town!

The competition was tough, but it was unthinkable that the Cultural Ministry should move to other quarters. The former government had bought the fine old family house and repaired it from top to bottom. We didn't eat lunch there, as there was no canteen. Nor did the employees want one. They had an excuse to go to some restaurant. Lately, as foodstuffs were growing scarce, we mostly went to Don Lalo's, two rooms that were more like a cave than anything else, with the inevitable checkered tablecloths and plastic carnations, and a piano in one corner. The owner, who had (imperceptibly to himself) grown fat on the remains of his guests' dishes, prided himself on his home cooking. Chicken broth with no chicken, salad with no oil, or seafood soup made with fish eyes that any gourmet could take for peppercorns, though my experienced palate easily recognized their flavour and rubbery consistency. Slippery little balls .... Dishes made from eyes of other kinds were further specialties of the chef. Steer's eyes, pigs' eyes, and as a particular treat, sheep's eyes, blue inside and softer and tastier than the rest.

At noon the whole neighbourhood met there: the civil servants, properly dressed, the whores, fresh from a good night's sleep, homosexuals with blond streaks in their hair, students from the School of Fine Arts, and Doña Cutu, a madam of indeterminate sex with a hoarse voice and well-trimmed moustache, who sat at the piano singing arias à la Mario Lanza. During lunch we would talk politics, or rather what to do about the country. Sometimes we spent the whole afternoon there. Then it would be five o'clock, time to punch out and walk home, of course, because the bus drivers had been on strike for a month. We always sat close to each other, used as we were to the promiscuity of sweaty legs and the emanations of other bodies and armpits. The atmosphere was really homey.

Sometimes our former boss would come by, a white-haired old man of around seventy-two who was sent to work at home while the Ministry tried to find a clause in the law that would allow them to retire him. He had been educated in Paris and London, and in his time had launched an important movement in painting. Nobody cared about the fact that he hadn't painted anything for the last ten years. Instead he had taken up raising dogs. And nobody seemed surprised when he turned up with his ten favourite lap-dogs in search of a bone someone might have left on a plate. He didn't find many. And the poor animals took it out on the customers, furiously licking their ankles. The old man's visits to the office were rare. Most of the time, when there were documents to sign, someone from our Ministry went to his home. (It was a garret crammed with paintings and strewn with the stinking turds of his dogs. Also to be seen: a photo of the first Chilean fireman. There he spent his days, remembering how, in Paris, in 1930, on a rainy night, Pablo Neruda had left him to pay the bill in the restaurant at the Gare de Lyon.) He was almost always drunk, and his clothes were nibbled away by the dogs. The law of bureaucratic immobility made it quite impossible to get rid of old employees. As a result we had two bosses, one old, one new. The new one was a poet: Guerrero, a young guy in a white suit with a finger-biscuit moustache. Self-taught, of humble origins. He blew in with the intention of changing the cultural landscape of Chile.

"Yes, Mr. Guerrero, I'm the new section head, the Ministry sent me," I explained.

He looked me up and down angrily, grumbling between his teeth something about the new President.

"I beg your pardon?"

"Your position is already filled," he went on.

After this lukewarm welcome he introduced me to a man of sixty-five or thereabouts who was drinking a cup of tea with lemon without making a sound. Don Lucas nodded in greeting. He looked at me. He had no desire to retire after his thirty-one years of silent service.

"There are no chairs!" he exclaimed.

I saw that this official had a chair, a typewriter, a telephone and a door with a lock which allowed him to shut himself in for the duration of the siesta, for as many hours as he pleased. His statement was like a death sentence, or rather a hint that I should set up my headquarters in the corridor. Hours, days, went by, and I still could do nothing but pace up and down my allotted corridor. But I mustn't become discouraged. I had waited so many years for a job.

The rest of the section I was supposed to manage consisted of five bureaucrats who put in their days in another room a little bigger than that of the boss. They represented sub-sections of my section. And they were, in turn, chiefs with no Indians. Their office had five enormous closet cupboards. Cupboards completely different from anything made nowadays. Oh yes! No good family of Chilean aristocrats in those days could be without cupboards with windows, mirrors and a couch, as well as room for a well-to-do person to dress and undress. The peculiar nature of the dressing-room in the early part of the century now made possible a step upward in the cultural development of our country. During the day, the bureaucrats were able to occupy their closets, stretch out on their couches and leave the section of sections unmanned. The door of the section of sections was opened only at ten in the morning when the sub-section heads drank tea with lemon.

One afternoon as I walked, deep in thought, down my corridor, I bumped into another section head, the one in charge of drama. He also was walking, reciting Goethe in German. By then I had but one powerful obsession: to get a chair on which I could sit out these cursed eight hours that earned me my salary.

"A chair!" Teodoro said.

"I've been walking up and down this corridor for three months. I'm getting varicose veins!"

He stared at me in a fury.

"You've just arrived and already you want a chair. I walked up and down here for fifteen years, and I didn't get my position back until after I died."

"What?" I was frightened.

"A joke in bad taste. I came back from holidays and found that the personnel had given me up for dead. They sent wreaths to my address, and money in an envelope. I don't know whose idea it was, but things grew so bad that I had to obtain a medical certificate saying I was alive. The boss, and the Minister himself, acting on some mysterious network of information, had given my job away to someone else. It took me two years to get my title back, and one grade lower at that!"

I wasn't going to put in two years in that corridor. The very next day I spoke to Guerrero.

"I can't go eight hours without a chair, in a place where every section and sub-section works behind closed doors. It shows a lack of respect. It's outrageous. I spent seven years at the university. I've a doctorate from the Sorbonne."

"What do you expect, miss, er . . . I'm not Jesus Christ to go around multiplying chairs. In this country half the work force is in the civil service, a million and a half people. Think about it!"

After such an exhibition of indifference there was nothing left to do but call the Minister. This was not easy. The secretaries who had been hired by the previous government, were protesting by not taking messages. I finally found his home number and managed to make an appointment for the thirty-first of the month.

An audience with a Minister was rather rare for the employees of the Ministry of Culture. Unheard-of, in fact, as I found out . . . One day as I left the office I found the National Symphony Orchestra rehearsing as they sat on the bumpers of cars parked in the alley. The violinists were stimulating their parts by making noises with their mouths. I asked them what this was all about. One of them said the instruments had all cracked open from the summer's dry heat.

"But that's ridiculous!" I said. "This can't go on. I'm going to speak to the Minister on the 31st, and . . . "

I had no time to finish my sentence when some bigmouth appointed himself the musicians' delegate to go along with me to the interview. By the time I had walked another block the news of my audience with the Minister had reached the head of Ballet, the head of Radio and the head of Publishing who came running down the alley with a list of petitions.

"But I'm going crazy, Mr. Minister, I've been three months in the place and haven't even got a chair!"

"Sometimes we'll be rehearsing and the dancers have to go out in the garden to pee behind the rosebushes. We just can't go on interrupting our work, sir. We need a powder room. We are professionals. And sometimes they do more than pee and the roses wilt, whatever the fertilizer experts say!"

"Do you see these growths on my lips, Mr. Minister? That's from playing scales without a violin. And there are eight of us suffering from these labial hernias!"

"And I happen to know, sir, that the radio equipment is all down at customs and has been for the last twenty-five years. It was donated after the Korean war and Supply never got it through customs."

"Yes, Mr. Minister, and we're about to bring out a pocket book but we've run out of paper . . . "

"That's enough of your begging!"

The Minister rose energetically from his chair and made it clear our talk was over. His final words were:

"We're using this year's Culture budget to buy rice. Let it

be understood. We have no foreign credit. The copper miners are on strike. What more can I tell you? We bought rice and the country ate it."

I had to find a chair, by hook or by crook. My varicose veins were getting worse. I couldn't go on like this. I was fed up with walking the corridor and glancing out the window from time to time at the erotic scenes in the neighbouring brothels. It was out-and-out obscene to see those fat moustachioed slobs taking off their clothes. I changed my tactics and began to make a few friends. I met Lucrecia who was in charge of Plastic Arts. And Elvira who was in the Radio section. Lucrecia lived in a room on that same alley, with a number of cats. That made it easy for her to get to work. She was no longer young, but had the energy and the style of dress of a fifteen-year-old. An out-dated fifteen-year-old, of course. Lots of eye make-up, mini-skirt, stockings with a seam and pointed shoes. Her fine, reddish-blonde hair flamed in the wind, its tint almost natural. We lunched together all the time. She told me she was a widow. Her brother was a captain in the guard. I told her I was an orphan with no relatives I knew of. She couldn't believe it.

"You don't even have an uncle around here?"

"Oh, sure, some kind of an uncle who tried to rape me when I was twelve, but that's all."

Lucrecia had cancer. Sometimes I wondered if it was catching. They had cut off both her breasts and now she had cotton stuffing instead. They had given her five years to live, and the five years were up, and more. And while we were telling our secrets the prostitutes were singing and drinking wine with oranges in it. A foul smell hung in the air. Something wrong with the drains. The whole neighbourhood of Mosqueto had been without water for two days. I wondered how Don Lalo was making his soup. But there was the fish soup, as usual.

After lunch we went to the Ministry library. It was very old. Mahogany panels with little stairs and stepladders for reaching the shelves. There were no books, of course, or if there were, they must have been in the hands of the Inventory people. Anyway, it was a nice place. Teodoro was declaiming Goethe in German (he was blond, a son of the settlers in the South who received land grants from the government in 1890). Teodoro was certain that he was "Werther" in person. Huachilao, a Mapuche Indian, was writing a dictionary in his corner.

"Seventy-five per cent of the Mapuches living in Santiago change their names," he said aggressively.

"At least you've got a chair," I remarked.

"I brought it from home," he answered.

I was not at all surprised to see him go for Teodoro's throat, shouting:

"Shut your mouth, you fucking Nazi! You racist . . . "

He was trying to kill him.

"Racist, racist!" shouted Huachilao.

We were trying to hold him back. I got kicked in the ankle. Lucrecia was shrilling like a squirrel. None of the employees came to help. Except Guerrero, who, very circumspectly, stuck his head in and said:

"Gentlemen, this place is like a whorehouse."

And he pulled them apart, saying to Huachilao:

"Come on, now, go back to your dictionary. Don't you know it's going to come out in our pocket series?"

Apart from Teodoro and his poetry, the library was a pleasant place.

Lucrecia had three passes to a movie house. I invited Don Lucas. I felt that the most important thing was to win him over, and at least find out what this section was supposed to do under my supervision. I should be sharing his office, and I meant to let him know as much. The movie was about the second world war. He showed little enthusiasm either for the film or its theme, but proudly demonstrated his theory that he could take an instant nap, any time, anywhere and in any circumstance. We made our way slowly out of the theatre. Pausing with the crowd, I asked him if he had liked the film. It was only a polite question, but it remained unanswered. Lucrecia suddenly screamed:

"It's the army! They're shooting!"

We heard more shots, and started to run. We ran as quickly as we could toward the hill of Santa Lucia. Maybe we were running toward the tanks! They sounded like wooden rattles. Stores and offices were closing. Where could we go? Where could we hide? A whole mob was running behind us like a herd of animals. Two or three of them fell. We could hear a confusion of shouts and cries. I didn't want to look. Don Lucas was so slow! I tried waiting for him but a bullet grazed my right arm. Good thing it wasn't my leg, I thought, running again. He was trotting clumsily along, his short, thin shanks barely able to carry his fat belly. I was starting to panic . . . when he was hit in the head. He fell like a sack of potatoes and let out a strange, choking sound. I stared at his head. It was bright red. I squatted beside him for a moment. Then I saw a tank. The crowd scattered. I caught a glimpse of Lucrecia going into a building with some other people. I ran and ran and managed to catch up with her. An attendant closed the grill. We were in an arcade of stores. I wanted to go up to another level. Go to a bathroom. Look at my arm by a proper light. I touched it. There was a hole in my coat, an opening with a little blood. Lucrecia screamed:

"Fascists! Murderers!"

Someone in the crowd said softly:

"It's a coup."

"Lucrecia, Lucrecia!" I called. "Let's get out of here!" And I began to run toward a stairway.

The stairs seemed to me the safest place, triple-reinforced concrete, made to withstand a quake. A burst of machine-gun fire shattered a window. Lucrecia had caught up with me now, limping. She had lost a shoe.

"Let's go to the underground parking!" I exclaimed.

We made our way down to the parking level in the dark. We stayed there the rest of the day, waiting. Lucrecia had some dried peaches in her purse, and we ate them. It was cold. We slept, or tried to. It was cold, and I couldn't forget the blood from Don Lucas's head. The thud on the pavement like a felled ox. A scab had formed on my arm. I scratched it. When things had been silent for a few hours we went out in the street. The grill was unlocked. It was dark. Everything was quiet. We met a policeman giving tickets to improperly parked cars. Trembling, we asked him what time it was.

"Five o'clock."

Five in the morning.

"What happened?" we asked.

"An army division attacked the president's palace, but the chief of staff crushed the rebellion."

Lucrecia was silent. I had trouble swallowing. We went to her place. We drank some coffee, not real coffee — fig coffee. The cats were ravenous. They jumped on my lap, looking for affection. The bathroom chose that night, of all times, to flood, and the downstairs neighbour, a known criminal who had never been jailed, came to complain that he was being dripped on. I turned off the tap. At least I could brush my hair. The radio didn't work.

At nine the next morning we crossed the street to the

office. The employees of the Ministry were lining up to punch their time cards. We took our place in the line, and suddenly Lucrecia exclaimed, sobbing:

"They killed Don Lucas!"

This was a frightful announcement. There was a general meeting in the library. Guerrero made a speech. The Union President, who showed up now for the first time, set up a committee for the defence of the building. Huachilao talked about a theory he had developed recently: the Mapuche Indians were descendants of the Greek gods. The burial was simple and brief. Guerrero recited his latest poem to his mistress. Then he made a brief allusion to Don Lucas as an admirable section head, and everyone sang the national anthem.

I was promoted to director. That is, my appointment became effective. I took possession of the office. And the chair.

The Union President phoned me. We had a brief and cautious conversation. He said he wanted to meet me next day in the cul-de-sac. Strange as it may seem, I went. He was dressed in black, and though it wasn't raining he wore a plastic raincoat.

"They're going to kill the President," he warned me in a whisper.

Then he wrote his phone number on a scrap of paper, and ran off down the alley, not toward the Ministry of Culture but toward a brothel. Before he reached the door he turned and cried, still running:

"Morning exercise!" and waved his pistol.

My new responsibilities as a boss made me forget the President of the Union. But I was filled with feelings of guilt over Don Lucas's death. I made up phrases as if I were helping him, as if I had waited for him. I remembered his head, red with blood on the pavement, and wanted to vomit. I decided instead to concentrate on getting my office in working order. The first thing was to make an inventory of all the existing material and find out what this damned section was supposed to do. My staff, from their cupboards, were reticent. They maintained that they had lost their keys. That the doors were barred. But I insisted, went ahead with my work anyway and I discovered a collection of giant photographic enlargements, no less, with Humphrey Bogart in "Casablanca" and Garbo in "Queen Christina" along with a series of posters announcing: "How to make our own film in ten easy lessons." It began to dawn on me that I might be in the Cinema section.

I found a theatre in the heart of the city, all boarded up, but with a few employees of the Ministry living in the front part, having divided the lobby with partitions into several rooms. Inside the theatre, buried under cobwebs and rubbish, lay all kinds of film-making equipment: cameras, lab material, sound recorders and what not else. Donated by the United Nations and carefully stored by Don Lucas year after year. The section had been in existence since 1928 and at the time had been the first film institute in Latin America. Since its foundation it had produced one film. A short in black and white, badly out of focus, where you could see today's cultural employees as they were thirty years ago, sitting at the same desks. They sat there in their grey suits, chatting. They were drinking lemon tea at ten in the morning during the screening of another film of other civil servants thirty years before who were also drinking lemon tea at ten in the morning . . . .

I tidied and cleaned and tried to put the theatre in order. All by myself. I got things more or less in shape, and sent a memo to the section employees making it compulsory to keep their doors open during office hours. Especially the doors of dressing-closets. Of course the memo disappeared into a vacuum. I was even accused of interrupting their work.

"What work?" I asked them, and they had no answer.

Guerrero brought in his mistress, his ex-wife, his best friend and his best friend's daughter as section heads for special projects. The newest employees were the representatives of the new government. There were not many of us: just Lucrecia, Elvira, Guerrero's friends, the Indian of Greek origin, the Union President and myself. We held meetings that went on for days and nights, discussing philosophical themes but also practical problems such as procuring olive oil or cigarettes.

One morning the Union President, looking worried, came up to me and said:

"It's your turn to stand guard."

So that night I stayed, along with some colleagues, to guard the building. Vigilance is the price of progress, and there we were, guarding, with whatever was at hand. Hammers, knives, and a few sharp forks. The Union President explained to us where the heart is located. Elvira and Lucrecia asked me:

"Wouldn't you be frightened, killing somebody with a sharpened table-fork?"

I wondered if I'd have time to use my fork if soldiers came with their machine guns. I was assailed by this doubt among many others. For example, I was surprised to recognize one of my section employees, owner of two buses, whose face I had seen in the film. I whispered to Lucrecia:

"What's he doing, mounting guard with us? Isn't he one of those who are paralyzing transportation in the country . . ."

The Union President said the heart was located just two

centimetres below the scapula.

"The scapula?" queried Elvira.

Lucrecia wanted to know if the blood all spurted out at once. Elvira was still looking for her scapula. The Union President showed us his pistol. For some reason it seemed to me like a lighter. He let us have no more than a glimpse of it, making it more mysterious. I was supposed to guard the second floor. I trembled there the whole night, thinking how the heart was two centimetres below the scapula, and that blood spurted out, dark red, like Don Lucas's head.

Guerrero called me in to his office and asked me to look after a delegation of foreigners that were touring the country. I organized a visit to our Ministry of Culture, including serving them coffee. I was very proud of having been given this responsibility. Coffee? There was no coffee. Nowhere. What was I going to do? I spied a secretary in one of the offices.

"Where can I get some coffee?"

"On the black market," she said, and hastily shut the door in my face.

I exhausted a number of theories as to why she had done so, though I was getting accustomed to closed doors. I supposed that the black market was a part of the city's central market place. I went to Mapocho, where a beggar was watching from the bridge, staring hungrily at the river rats. Big rats, A cross between rats and cats.

"Where's the black market?" I asked.

The beggar took off his dark glasses. He had fair skin and freckles. He had no legs, and got around on a board with skate rollers under it. I remembered seeing him when I was a child. It seemed to me his hair had grown thicker. I said to him:

"I know you. You used to stay at the corner of Monjitas

and San Antonio. And we used to play in the elevator of the building. Don't you remember?"

He stared at me. I didn't insist. Then he started laughing like a madman.

"The black market!" he almost shouted. "It's run by the stores, the store owners themselves!"

And he went back to the edge of the bridge to watch the rats.

I went into a store. An old woman in black, grumbling and frowning, sold me coffee at fifteen times the set price.

The foreigners looked jolly and healthy. Our little celebration took place in the library. There were eight Soviet citizens wearing grey raincoats. The bureaucrats emerged from their caves. For the first time I realized that there were about a hundred of us in the Ministry of Culture building.

"Look at the clothes!" they said to each other, laughing, as if they were discovering for the first time that the "bad guys" owned something they could envy.

A slim, blonde actress, her fame well-established in the Socialist world by thirty films, had all the men going crazy. Guerrero, still dressed in white with a carnation in his buttonhole, talked about the beauty of Chilean women, although he meant to say Soviet. Afterwards he danced a tango with the actress, while the employees begged for the Chilean national dance.

"A cueca, boss, a cueca."

Paying no attention to them, Guerrero sang "Muñeca Brava" in the manner of Carlos Gardel. The guests had brought some vodka, and we drank vodka and talked about future projects. Massive cultural exchanges and astronomical sums of money were floating in the air. Guerrero suddenly became aware of his previous lapse about beautiful Chileans, and launched into an even more disconcerting speech:

"Chilean women are all horrible, dark little things with fat bellies, no ass and skinny legs, regardless of class."

"Must be the vodka," someone murmured, and I thought what an impression the visitors would have of us. But Guerrero went on to recite a poem, very sure of himself:

"Man is like the animals.
He starts out early making love,
first like a pigeon, circling
around his prey, then giving
a harmless little peck.
Later he turns cat, and
loves with tooth and claw,
and later still, an adult,
slow as an old post-horse,
he races for thirty seconds
and rests as many hours.
Lastly, he's like a dog:
He sniffs, raises his leg . . . and leaves.

I don't know where Guerrero classed himself, but in any case the delegation left with what remained of the vodka, after signing a very vague agreement. I should mention that it was not Guerrero who signed but our former boss who came in at the last moment with no shirt on. It was his dog's paw that stamped the paper, thus sealing this international encounter.

"Let's go to the demonstration and forget this place," Lucrecia said to me. "There are a lot of young guys there."

We went to her room and dolled ourselves up a little. She put makeup on her legs and pencilled in a seam on the back of her calves.

"Nobody wears stockings with seams," I told her.

"So what!" she answered.

I wondered if it was all the makeup she used that had given her cancer. We went out carrying our placards. The Alameda was one big party. Half a million people.

I remembered Don Lucas. We chatted with a few boys. Lucrecia was happy as a kid. She lifted up her skirt without really intending to. How old was she, anyway? Fifty-five? There was a blond French boy with the face of an angel. She whispered in my ear, with the firm voice of experience:

"He's a pretty boy, but he can't get it up."

I stared at his angel face which was more like that of a timid devil.

"I'm a former priest," he told us.

The boys moved on, and we continued our stroll.

I walked eleven kilometres to get home that night. I lived in a modern two-room studio, low-rent, in the Providencia neighbourhood. My building was one of the tallest in the city, but was still without an elevator after all this time. And the only company that sold them had decided to fold when the new President came to power. The tenants were all still awake, pounding furiously on their saucepans. The lights, with children at the switches, went on and off like Christmas trees. All this at one in the morning. Others were burning a bus in the street to protest against the government. The flames shot high but the volunteer firemen didn't come. After climbing fourteen flights of stairs in my worn-out shoes I saw my neighbour through his open door. (A good family man with seven kids, he went to Mass every Sunday.) He very kindly invited me to have a cup of tea, and showed me his new invention. He was making "miguelitos" — nails twisted together for throwing under tires. I told him it had been delightful and went across to my apartment and called the police. I told them what was going on. The duty officer laughed:

"If he's who I think he is, he's my boss's cousin." He paused. "Have you got a car, miss?"

"No."

"Then what the hell are you worried about?"

He hung up.

The hammering of saucepans went on all night. I was hungry, but I had nothing to eat. I took a bit of powdered milk I still had and mixed it with water. I was hungry as ever.

Next day I walked the eleven kilometres again on an empty stomach. All the way to the office. As if he had guessed, the employee who owned the buses had brought me some meat. Horsemeat, he said, correcting himself. He invited me for dinner that night. All this bothered me, because the drivers were still on strike, but I accepted . . . because of the food. I told Lucrecia and she said:

"Got to watch out for those old guys, my girl!"

The old guy took me in one of his vehicles to Stop number 12 on the Gran Avenida. That's where he lived. His wife was paralytic and his two sons were one-armed. The dog had eaten the other two arms. He had a big house. With pool. And a bower of wild grapevines. From her wheel-chair the woman stared as if she were ashamed not to be able to move or speak. I greeted her normally, as if nothing was wrong. We sat down at the dinner table. The boys had prepared the meal. They were incredibly ingenious in using their toes. They could pick up anything. They could even cut the meat. Horsemeat with rice. It tasted good. I was so hungry . . . I could have eaten anything. I didn't say a word. Nor did the family. I kept wondering why they had invited me. The sons went to bed, the mother stayed in a corner and the owner of the buses went to sleep in an armchair. I left, and walked and walked, right to the city centre.

I lived so far away that at times I spent the night at Lucrecia's place. I opened the door and found her sleeping. She got up, all dishevelled. Her hair was growing-in grey. The blonde, fine, well kept hair-do was like a straw mat. She knew what I was thinking.

"I couldn't find any dye in this whole town," she said in a pitiful voice.

She went back to bed. I curled up in a corner of the room with two purring cats to keep me company and a whole family of fleas.

We woke early. That day Lucrecia was to queue up for rice. It was four in the morning. I was dead tired. My feet were swollen.

"Oh, I need some rice, too!" I exclaimed.

Off we went in the dark. The street lamps were out. Trying to recognize the streets. She had insisted on bringing along a couple of cats in case we found a garbage can with food in it. The sale was supposed to be in a rice-packaging plant down by the Mapocho River district, near the railway tracks. When we got there a number of people had already arrived and were standing in line. They had coats on and carried lanterns, and some had folding chairs. Two of them were listening to a battery radio turned down low. We squatted down with the cats. Dawn was coming. The lineup was growing. Some were sleeping, others playing cards. At eight o'clock the porter at the packaging plant came out to say the rice would not be given out today, but tomorrow. By that time there were two hundred of us. One of the cats ran away. We'd have to stay in this same queue until tomorrow. I told Lucrecia I'd go and punch us both in at the office so they couldn't dock our pay. Then I walked to the office. It was empty. I punched in at ten to nine and left a note saying I'd be back. I felt a vague unease. I'd have to get my section going no matter what. But I was hungry. I'd grown thin. I started back toward the rice depot. On the way I noticed a lineup and ran to join it. It was a short one, only ten people. I imagined all kinds of good things. Surely one of them would be there. I'd get something, at any rate. When I reached the booth it turned out to have cigarettes. Delighted, I bought two packs, though I don't smoke. Finally I got back to Lucrecia. She'd almost lost our place by chasing the cat. She finally found it eating cockroaches in the Company garbage bin. The people in the lineup were staring at my cigarettes. Aloud, but not insistently, I said:

"I'll trade them for food."

One man gave me two loaves of bread for three cigarettes. For half a dozen I got some oranges and a hard-boiled egg. We ate. Then I went to sleep right on the ground holding the poor cat by the tail so it couldn't run away. Between dreams I heard Lucrecia whispering to other women about more food.... We spent all that day and the following night in the line. Once, while we were sleeping, one of the cats went astray, this time for good. Lucrecia kept repeating:

"Oh, I do hope she finds a house where there's food. The poor thing!"

"It was a tabby?"

I was surprised.

"Yes, a she. This is her son."

She meant the one who was still with us.

There was an hour to wait until the sale started. People were stretching, wiping their eyes or quietly combing their hair. Suddenly eight young men appeared. Their hair was wild, their pants were tight-fitting. They had knives in their hands. Not really knives. They were long, sharp awls. They let the air out of the tires of several cars belonging to people in the line. Then they attacked the people closest to the wicket of the rice-packing plant and tore their clothing, laughing.

"Forget about the lineup!" they shouted.

"Who are they, anyway," Lucrecia asked.

"They are the Q boys," someone said. "They come early and take people's places in the queue. Then they re-sell the rice on the black market."

One of them came up to Lucrecia and with his awl killed the cat she was holding. She was all splashed with blood. She howled like a madwoman.

"Savage! You savage!"

A little farther on I saw a man getting into a parked car. I caught Lucrecia by one arm and said:

"Run, run or they'll kill us. Idiot!"

We ran to the car. She was bawling. I pushed her into the stranger's car and locked the door.

"Take off, will you? Fast?" I begged him.

He was at least as nervous as we were. He started the motor just as two Q boys arrived pointing their awls at his tires. He couldn't get the car moving.

"In reverse, in reverse!" I screamed.

He took off in reverse. Lucrecia and I hardly spoke during the whole ride. But her awful weeping quieted down. We went to her apartment. I thought about the office. Had to get that section working.

"We have to go to work, Lucrecia," I said softly.

"What do I care about all that shit. I want my cats!"

I tried to console her:

"You just have to get used to it. This is war! And you still have three."

But she started throwing books and other things at the wall, and broke a window. The known but unimprisoned criminal came up to complain. We were astonished to hear some strange noises in the city, like a bombardment, then isolated shots and the sound of machine gun fire. The criminal fetched his radio. We heard the announcement that this was the only station broadcasting in the country. From now on it was to be called the armed forces station.

"This time it's happened," said the criminal.

"The coup?" Lucrecia exclaimed.

We looked out the window and saw the street full of soldiers in green uniforms. They were searching the area. The criminal looked worried.

"I'm afraid," I said.

He took pity on us and said:

"Come with me."

We went down to his apartment and shut ourselves up in a kind of storage room. From outside you couldn't see it was there. Inside it was very well equipped. A radio with earphones, a butane cooker, water, tea, biscuits. We heard the heavy footsteps of soldiers outside. We held our breath. They broke down the front door. We were shaking in our boots. I thought I'd faint. What were we doing in this pantry with a known criminal? I had done nothing bad. I'd only tried to put a little order in a section that reported not to me but to my boss, who reported to the former boss, who reported to the Minister, who reported to the President and the President to the Congress.... Just then we heard a soldier's voice:

"Nobody here."

There's either whores or cats or nothing at all," said another. "I wouldn't mind hurting somebody right now. Give a scare to one of those no-good bums."

"Hey! Look! Here's a record, I'm taking this one for my brother."

They went off, laughing. The front door of the apartment must have been left open. We could hear distant voices for some time. The criminal was toying with a pointed dagger. Its glint was all you could see in the dark pantry. Lucrecia broke the silence to ask him if the newspaper stories about him were true.

"My ass!" he said.

My hands and feet were trembling with the cold. I was getting a chill. When would this interminable moment, this long day, come to an end? I put on the earphones. Squeezed Lucrecia's arm. They were announcing a curfew. No one was to go out in the street. We opened the door of our hiding place. The soldiers had hung a white sheet in the window.

We went up to Lucrecia's apartment. The cats were there. Everything was upside-down. A white sheet had been hung in her window as well. The criminal came up to see us again, very excited. He said they had killed the President. He had managed to pick up this news from Argentinian shortwave.

I slept and slept, for eighteen hours. Lucrecia cried a lot.

Two days later I went out into the street. I was arrested at the first corner. They asked for my identification and told me to put my hands up. I had no cards on me. It was a little fleck of cat's blood on my clothing that made them suspicious. Along with a tall man and a small woman, they took me off in a jeep. Our eyes were blindfolded and we were driven far outside the city. I don't know where. For no reason they made me take my clothes off, then tied me down on a table. They put rings on my fingers and toes. At first I didn't know what they were for, but it hurt very much and made me jerk and shit and bite my lips. I could taste the salty blood and feel my torn gums. Afterwards I realized it had been electric shocks. They inserted a mouse's tail in my vagina and took off my blindfold so that I could watch. I felt like a hole for the disposal of excrement, my body was limp, exhausted, weak and breathless. They accused me of being an agitator stirring up violence in the country, and a member of a clandestine organization for the defence of the late President. And an international agent subverting democracy. For no apparent reason they let me go thirty days later. They gave no explanation. I didn't go back to see Lucrecia. I knew that Elvira had gone mad. They had killed the Union President. Guerrero turned out to have been a stool-pigeon. They split open the Minister's head and he remained alive for a few days in this condition defending the Ministry. Some of the other Ministry employees, the ones that dated from the old, old government, are still there, motionless in their cupboards. A few of them, to avoid paying rent — life being so expensive — have given up their own houses and moved permanently into the Culture Ministry. I don't envy them. I'm finally convinced that blind alleys are sinister places of evil omen.

Voyage to the Other Extreme

I COULDN'T stand his finger. Not because it was short and thick and strangely proportioned, but because it hovered over the keyboard with such agonizing delays. And his eyes! He would look up suddenly, revealing red, crawling veins like my uncle Beto's, then go back to searching among the keys. What was more, I was irked by his illiterate voice pronouncing each letter, laboriously, until he found it on the Underwood.

He asked my name and asked my name again. I began to wonder what it was. This process went on for several days. The snot-green colour of his uniform gave me the shivers. The uniform was green, the walls were green, and the typewriter, and the photo of the president of the new régime, and the wet towel that hung on the back of a door.

The man was writing my name, my address, my occupation, the number of my identity card, my tax-file number, my electoral registration, my driver's licence and my last tax declaration. He was spare and scrawny, with a face so thin that it seemed his nose might twist in a high wind. The other two, in contrast were young and chubby with the fat of rice-eaters, dark-skinned, their collars strewn with dandruff.

The silence was broken only by the clacking of the keys, the questions, and, from time to time, a piercing scream from other prisoners being maltreated. I was tired. My eyelids were swollen. I was nervous. The corners of my lips twitched uncontrollably.

"Can you type?" the man asked suddenly. I nodded.

"Finish this," he ordered. He'd had enough.

I sat down and typed my own vital data on a sheet of squared paper. Then I returned to my chair in the middle of the room.

An officer, tall and impressive, burst in. He shouted:

"Leave this dumb bugger alone!"

And he marched off like the lord of the land.

One of the young soldiers spoke to the typist:

"Y'only need those papers for the ones that were tortured!"

The typist pointed his finger at me, exclaiming:

"Can'tya see the cigarette burns on his face, stupid?"

The young one looked at me, abashed. They made me sign a smeared sheet of paper with my name handwritten in one corner at the top. The paper said that they had inflicted no kind of violence, physical or psychological, on myself or my family. The soldier returned my documents along with a white slip of paper setting me free.

"You can go," he said.

I stood up, dazed, and made my way timidly to the door as if I were in a nightmare with a happy ending. A "free man," I walked down a hallway piled with prisoners' belongings. I was thinking of searching out my small suitcase when two men in uniform came from the opposite direction carrying on their shoulders a corpse without ears. I was shaken by an irresistible shudder... I gave up the idea of my search. In the doorway I gave my slip of paper to the guard with an intimidated glance, still fearing a last-minute disaster. What a day! The blue sky and the snow-capped mountains — a real Swiss postcard! I didn't know what time it was. The air was hot and dry. The road was dusty and in my rubber boots my feet soon acquired great blisters. Someone came toward me on horseback. We eyed each other warily. I recognized him, and he knew me. He was a miner from our group, the man in charge of the dynamite. A plump, sturdy fellow with small, shifty eyes. He had dark hair and a pleasant crop of freckles. I wanted to speak to him. Tell him I'd been set free. Real luck! But he looked right through me. I turned. Shouted to him:

"Comrade Fidel!"

He pulled over in my direction, frightened, and without dismounting said in a low voice:

"Better not to know each other."

Then he stripped off the shirt he was wearing and threw it to me, exclaiming, "It's dangerous going around like that!" — and rode off at a gallop.

I changed there and then. My old shirt, in shreds from my interrogations, I tossed into some bushes, glancing around to make sure I wasn't seen.

I arrived in the town. I went to the store. The owner, a woman with big breasts hanging out, false eyelashes and a skirt that bore the marks of successive adaptations to the fashion in vogue, greeted me with a smile. She said:

"Why, isn't that nice, to see you back!"

I went through to the bathroom, urinated and washed my face. I was pale. I combed my hair and saw the round scars of two cigarette burns on my right cheek. I touched them. Then I went out to the store again. The woman poured me a glass of wine, fluttering her detachable lashes and giving a sensual laugh:

"Here's to freedom, democracy and order!"

"Weren't you in the party and the J.A.P.?" I asked, innocently.

She came closer and laid a hand on my shoulder. She explained, in a husky, insinuating voice:

"My dear, last month was different. A national bankruptcy. Nobody was working. Look, just take the factory down at the corner. At three in the afternoon the workers all left to join the demonstrations. Even the cats were out parading!"

She paused.

"Now we're getting back to normal," she went on. "The people have been very generous in cooperating to rebuild the nation. Right now there's a feeling of gratitude toward the Armed Forces and the Guards that's not easy to put down. Let's have a little drink to them."

I refused. I brushed her arm from my shoulder and left without a word.

I was walking alone. People stayed locked up in their houses maintaining order and the newly established discipline. I came to the sidewalk in front of my house. By chance a military patrol was there inspecting it. I walked on without a pause. A little farther on at a service station were trucks full of uniformed men on alert. A white Peugeot stopped and a blond man with a moustache offered to give me a lift downtown. I accepted. Suddenly I felt happy. From his clothing and the Medical Academy symbol—a white serpent — stuck to his windshield, I supposed that he was a member.

"You a doctor?" I asked, to start the conversation, seeking a kindred soul in that besieged city.

"I'm going to the military hospital," he answered calmly.

"And how are things there these days?" I asked, as if we were talking about a completely everyday situation.

"So-so," he replied, staring over the steering-wheel.

"Many wounded soldiers?" I asked.

"No, the other side," he replied, and, as if he wanted to get to the point, turned toward me and scrutinized me. He must have been encouraged to go on by the fact that I had chestnut hair:

"The great problem at the moment is mattresses!"

"Mattresses?" I was surprised.

"We have orders not to waste our plasma reserves on people who've ruined the country. Of course they're lying there bleeding to death. The hospital beds are a complete write-off."

He braked to a halt and went on in a more confidential tone:

"There you're soaked with the smell of blood from top to bottom. Not only that: the dying relieve themselves unconsciously. We've been waiting there all week for the garbage trucks to come and take away the corpses. But there was a delay in getting an order and an official memo from the general in charge. Finally the trucks came and were loaded with carcasses. That was a big job for the poor soldiers, emptying the beds and loading the garbage trucks. Nobody knows if it was the quantity or the weight or some mysterious thing, but the trucks couldn't move off. Maybe a spare parts problem, or sabotage by extremist groups. You can't imagine the flies and larvae that have reproduced in the last week. What I need is a good vacation from it all. Stay in Florida till all this blows over...."

We were driving along the Alameda. I asked to get out, and said good-bye. Contreras' house was in a cross street. A garden, a bungalow. I rang the bell. No one answered. Then I sensed that someone was approaching inside, stealthily, as if they didn't want to be heard from the street. I pounded the door, saying:

"Contreras! It's me, Antonio!" The door opened on the chain. Contreras looked pale and greenish. He was nervous. He stammered:

"I've got five children! You can't stay here! They're combing the neighbourhood!"

He shut the door. Five minutes left until curfew. I ran. I ran, and thought of Lucia. She lived a few blocks away. My body felt limp. My slack muscles couldn't get up much speed. But there was Lucia's familiar building at last, a three-story building. As I reached the entrance I heard helicopters searching from the air for subversive extremist groups, firing scattered bursts from their machine-guns. Lucia lived on the second floor. She had a small, two-room apartment. A bed. A crocheted counterpane and an enormous red butterfly. There was a man who greeted me as if I'd just discovered his hideout. Lucia brought me a dish of string-bean salad and the cat jumped up on me, spilling the beans on my trousers. Lucia apologized, saying:

"She's in heat."

"She picked her up, laid her in her lap and began caressing her in a most unusual way, from neck to tail, while the pussy purred with delight.

I ate. I had a shower, and Lucia loaned me a pair of pants and other clothing that belonged to her brother. I shaved.

I was surprised to hear from her that my full name had appeared on the latest list of people wanted by the new government. She advised me to ask at once for asylum in some diplomatic mission. Pick any embassy in the phone book and go like a robot to its front entrance. Once in the embassy grounds, my troubles would be over. If that didn't work, and I was stuck in front of the embassy I'd chosen, I should examine the houses next door. Look for big trees with thick foliage. Climb one of them and suddenly, from a branch that was not too fragile, drop inside without a second thought. Another good way was to have a contact in the diplomatic world. Explain the situation to him and I'd be home free.

But in the meantime I was imagining another way, tramping across the mountain range carrying nothing but a water canteen; then, suddenly, those eternal snows that freeze your ears, your toes and your balls. I'd need to carry a penknife, like the conquistadors who had had to cut off their frozen sexes and throw them down a gorge. What a splendid tribute to Pedro de Valdivia and the discovery of Chile!

Then I thought of something more practical, such as a Caravelle with muzak and a blonde serving me a whiskey with bread and butter. (Bread and butter and Nescafé.) Arriving thus in the People's Republic of Albania, or (just my luck!) ending up for the rest of my life in North Korea. Learning Korean!

I called Sara but there was no answer.

I went and cuddled up beside Lucia. I liked Lucia. I don't know if I loved her or not. What I did know was that I felt tense and couldn't sleep, but all night long I saw fat Suarez with his head split in two. With a hole in his skull and blood running out. It was like a broken flower pot, and the brains were gone. I returned to Lucia's body beside me, soft, white, fresh from the winter. But fat Suarez came back. I saw him in a silent close-up, as in a horror film, with the expression of a madman. His head shattered, like opaque glass, quite empty. It was hard to erase from my thoughts the way they had cracked his skull with their gun-butts. I almost screamed.

But I got up in silence and went to piss. Lucia said:

"Shhh, the neighbours!"

I went back to bed. I dozed a little.

At nine next morning I sat down at the phone and called an acquaintance: John John, consul of the Land of the Other Extreme. I spoke to him, word for word, as follows:

"Hello Mister John. I'll make this as quick as possible. This is a delicate business. Do you know my voice? I can't say my name on the phone just now. I'm on the faculty." (I couldn't say which one.) "My problem is, I'm on the newspaper list..." (I couldn't mention the date.) "... of people wanted by the new regime to suffer capital punishment. They may reduce the sentence to thirty-two years of voluntary labour. But I have my doubts about that. Do you hear me? John John, I need a safe place."

John John gave me his address.

I tried a last call to Sara and then said good-bye to Lucia and the man discovered in his hideout. I went out to the street and took a bus.

I paid for my ticket and noticed that the price had quadrupled. The bus was full of silent people. This was strange. Let's just say, I like conversations in buses. Several incidents attracted my attention. First of all, two old men, their clothing torn and their bodies and faces covered with bruises, boarded the bus by the front steps. Everyone looked around, disconcerted. The men seemed weary. They looked poor, skinny and sickly. Someone said:

"Those ones came from the Stadium."

Silence came over the bus for a moment. The two men with the torn clothes and bruises got off. Then another guy with grey hair and big ears and an obsessed and timid look worked his way toward a young girl sitting in the second seat from the front. Because of the press of standing passengers and the constant swaying of the bus, the man's groin began to swell like a balloon, until a passage was forced through his zipper, which had come open through some mysterious process. The seated girl, dreaming, awoke to this sight and emitted a strangled cry. The man moved away from her as fast as he could. A fat, irritable lady screamed:

"Arrest him! Arrest him! He's an extremist!"

But another voice from among the passengers exclaimed:

"Be careful! He's a pervert and he's got a razor-blade!"

The girl was crying and the obsessed man got off the bus. Rumours of all kinds made the rounds but suddenly ceased when a circumspect officer climbed aboard, also by the front entrance, and looked with disgust at the passengers packed so promiscuously together.

Paying attention to all these goings-on, I got off two stops late. I arrived at John John's at the very moment when he, by a strange coincidence, was giving a garden party. Some diplomats and foreigners were discussing the political situation. Helicopters, like porpoises, passed overhead from time to time, relentlessly searching out clandestine organizations and subversive concentrations from the air. Three of the diplomat's guests were leaders of a civilian organization for the defence of democracy through military coups. They were proud and happy, showing around certain neat-looking light carbines just in from Brazil. One of these men was a fur wholesaler and the other two owned a shoe factory. Everyone was speaking English. A blonde, dressed in tweed, looking as if she had stepped out of a British Airways ad, came up and offered me a drink. I wanted milk, I wanted café au lait. Something nourishing. But she gave me a gin and ginger. Two Australian girls looking like boy scouts and wearing blue jeans were sending me signals from a corner. They were wearing knapsacks and had the look of people who had paid two thousand dollars for plane tickets to an exotic adventure, exciting and dangerous. I went over to them. I have never been interested in sports. One of them related how a bullet had grazed her forehead, and showed me her scar. The other tried to make me understand in laborious Spanish that the hospitals were not very efficient here. What a revelation. Just then John John came by and greeted me. He had been talking to the Ministry of Foreign Affairs of his country, and he looked worried. He led me to another corner of the room and whispered in my ear:

"Do you think your life is in danger?"

He took me by surprise. I assured him that it was true, and even went so far as to repeat to him in a tone of mingled pride and apprehension:

"I'm on the new government's wanted list."

This satisfied him ipso facto. He took me in his car to the official residence of the embassy. There a majordomo in white gloves and with an effeminate voice, accompanied by two grey poodles, met us at the door. They took me up to the third floor. It was an elegant house with an abundance of crystal chandeliers, Persian carpets and paintings in carved frames that were worth more than the pictures. We arrived in the servant's quarters. In one of the rooms were fourteen people waiting to leave the country. They were sitting around on a few mattresses packed into the floor space. People were half-dressed, and clothing was drying in the windows. They all looked at me with curiosity. I greeted them, shaking hands and saying my name distinctly. Someone said:

"We're short a mattress."

The majordomo asked for two volunteers to carry a piece of foam rubber from a neighbouring room. Two men volunteered. I said good-bye to John John and he gave me a pack of cigarettes. When he left they all asked me for a cigarette. Some, in their enthusiasm, took two. I was left with an empty package. I crumpled it up and threw it on the floor. A pregnant woman looked fixedly at me and exclaimed:

"Today's my turn for cleaning. If the men would lend a hand it would really help."

A priest came over and introduced himself as Juan de la Capilla, a foreigner. He broke his cigarette in two and gave me half. With equally good intentions he invited me to perform some physical exercises, counting:

"One, two, one, two..."

Another woman, of excessive and maternal obesity, asked me, with an inquisitive but friendly air, my motive for visiting this retreat. For some reason I began telling how I had been arrested. Perhaps because she approached me with eyes that were caressing and affectionate. She explained that she was collecting people's stories for publication in the international press when we got out. Everything was mixed up in my head. Little by little my story came out:

At first, I remembered, I was on the ground all day with a blanket over my head and they wouldn't let me see. Then, with my head still covered, I was taken to a closed-in place where I was blindfolded with a black handkerchief and seated on a chair. One person interrogated me first. He didn't hit me. Then another one came and punched me in the kidneys and kicked my shins. He said to me, "You're a tough one," and then tied me with cords to an armchair and six of them interrogated me. They gave me electrical shocks in the hands and body. There were heavy rings on my fingers. The rings were connected to electric wires and every time they turned on the juice it hurt. I'd jump in my seat and bite my lips and tongue. They gave me shocks all over my body. In the heart, the testicles, the legs. I'd scream and scream and they'd make me shut up.

"What about your head?" asked the woman.

"No, not in the head," I answered.

One of the refugees came over. He was an old man, about seventy, with grey hair and a hawk nose. He bent his head to be sure he could hear my tale. He said:

"In my village I saw the fascists cut off people's feet and make them walk on their stumps through the streets."

He had a strong Spanish accent. I asked him:

"Are you Spanish?"

"No. Aragonese," he replied.

Then, violently and waving his arms like a dwarfish vampire, he exclaimed:

"I saw them shooting people in the bullring and the young gentlemen applauded. They stoned my sister to death. That was in the Civil War."

I was tired. I fell asleep. At intervals, awakening, I saw the half-naked bodies on the mattresses. You could hear bursts of machine-gun fire. I dreamed I had a demon in my belly, biting, punching, burning in a thousand ways. I felt dizzy, I had a headache and pains in my back. My voice had changed its timbre and sounded now menacing, now sardonic, and all night I seemed to talk of erotica in a way that was, for me, most unusual. I was overcome by an arctic cold. My hands were freezing and no longer felt pain. My tongue seemed coated, my breath was foul, I dreamed that I vomited, and felt my stomach bloated. I woke up howling. In the dark a shadow came near me. It said:

"My name's Vargas. I'm a doctor. What's wrong?"

I couldn't tell him. We spoke softly so as not to wake the others. As if he had guessed, he asked:

"Nervous?"

I stammered a denial.

"Wait!" he said.

He straightened up and went away. He returned with a glass of water and said:

"Here's a valium."

I swallowed it. The water tasted like toothpaste. I think I was hungry, nothing more. Next morning we had breakfast in the room. The majordomo, in his elegant suit and white gloves, pushed in a little table on wheels, with porcelain coffee cups and one slice of toast per person very nicely served. He announced that several bombs had exploded in a bus filled with soldiers.

Later came a diplomatic employee with a face like a barnyard fowl, in a well-pressed suit and a polka-dot tie. He made us sign a paper in which it was stipulated that the cost for each one of us was fifteen dollars a day. Just about my monthly salary. In some remote future we would pay it back to the embassy. As the employee explained to us, this was a pure formality, a means by which his Excellency the Ambassador would be able to claim for the personal money he had invested in these people who were for the moment not gainfully employed.

Afterwards, in the course of the same day, I had the honour of meeting the Ambassador and his wife, who didn't shake hands with me. On the contrary, they seemed to practise a totally Anglo-Saxon indifference. They explained briefly in broken Spanish that this was an emergency situation to which they would do their best to adapt. The important thing was for the group to remain in this room because of possible denunciation by the neighbours.

"No one must know that you are here," the lady stated nervously. Then she went on to describe the customs of the house.

"We are very meticulous about cleanliness, " she told us,

and went on reciting rules like a maiden aunt. "Ashes must go in ash-trays. Towels are for drying yourself. The toilet must be flushed after use. Paper napkins should be used only for wiping the mouth."

She brought her speech to a close by making a present to each of us of a red tooth-brush. She also loaned us dominoes, a chess set and a couple of decks of cards. Vargas, in perfect public-school English, asked the Ambassador what was new in the city. He replied that the embassies were full of partisans of the fallen government. Also, three or four of the most spacious churches in the city had been the cause of a bottle-neck in the public sewage system of the city, as a result of the tremendous number of souls to whom they had given asylum (more than twenty thousand) and nourished with powdered milk for the past month. The said souls, apart from the constraints of space and the fact that they were piled in on top of each other, were suffering from collective and chronic diarrhea. It was hoped this situation would be relieved with the help of the International Red Cross and certain lady volunteers from the upper levels of society (who wanted to make a good impression on the new government). These places of refuge gave off such an odour that it was impossible to drive within twenty blocks of them.

I suppose it was news of this kind that had provoked Mrs. Ambassador's speech on meticulous hygienic practices in that house. In any case, as if specialization were the secret art of running the diplomatic world in these unusual circumstances, our residence persisted in producing pea soup and nothing else, both at lunch and dinner. The small ration of one ladle of soup was enough to induce our nocturnal machine-gun fire; strange sounds, reverberating cannonades and nauseating smells made me, on certain nights, dream that I was in hell. The majordomo, though he always found us sitting on our mattresses to eat, never, I must admit, infringed the rules of etiquette. He brought us each a complete setting of silver with two forks and two knives. Two glasses. One for wine and the other for water. He served us as if we were seated at the most elegant of tables, always from the left, with his white gloves, and a serviette, also white, was draped over his right arm.

I decided to join Juan de la Capilla in his morning exercises. He told me he had been arrested for having a Chilean flag in his sacristy. Another priest he had known, a Spaniard, had been found floating dead in the Mapocho River. His face had been gnawed by mice. Juan de la Capilla would exclaim:

"Relax, now, relax! Relax your toes, relax your ankles, relax your calves, relax your knees, relax your chest, relax your fingers... relax your head!"

There we were on our beds of waiting, doing exercises so that our muscles wouldn't stiffen up.

Vargas passed out valium pills as if they were after-dinner mints. As he offered them he would say:

"Mild, very mild. At the Psychiatric Hospital we give as many as eight a day to the patients."

From this I supposed that he was a psychiatrist. The pregnant woman with the weak but determined voice exclaimed:

"I know that one of us is working for the CIA."

We looked around at each other, while her husband took her gently by the arm and guided her to the edge of a foam mattress, where they sat down and began holding hands.

A girl of ten was playing cards with a very tall man; his thinness had an oriental, unhealthy quality. He was wearing a checked shirt. They were both on one of the mattresses. I overheard the following conversation:

"João, why do you look so grumpy all the time?"

"Because I am!" he said in a nasal accent.

"Smile, just once!" begged the child, her eyes wide and supplicating.

João tried a smile, but it came out exaggerated, twisted and sad. It revealed luminous, metallic teeth, black as a limousine.

The child was inspired to ask further questions. This time she wanted to know why he didn't have bone teeth like humans. João replied that in Brazil they had pulled them out one by one during his twenty-eight months in prison.

"I had to get a plate," he said.

The girl went on, unperturbed:

"My grandmother has a plate, too, and every night she puts them in a glass of water so they don't shrink."

She paused.

"Why didn't you get white ones?" she asked.

"These are cheaper," he replied, going on with their game. A moment later I heard him say:

"No cheating, Margarita!"

My mattress lay beside that of the pregnant woman, and at night she would sit up and stare at me as I was trying to have a nap. Just when I was dropping off she would roll over on top of me with all her weight, waking me up. Her husband told me they came from Valparaiso. An old mummified witch had informed on them for some trumped-up offence. They had been under arrest for a few hours, and then were allowed to go home. What a surprise it had been to see the old witch, his stool-pigeon, hanging from the lamp post in front of his own house.

"Holy Virgin! A miracle!" I exclaimed.

"Ach, I'm Jewish, I don't believe in that stuff," he said calmly.

Next day we had a visit from John John, who explained

that he had undertaken certain measures to have us moved to other diplomatic missions, but the results of his negotiations had not been entirely successful. That same day I washed my undershorts and spent the whole morning with a towel wrapped around me. I didn't do my exercises for fear some movement might reveal to the child a glimpse of my private parts. There was a rumour to the effect that certain generals who supported the late President had organized an army and were marching on the capital. I heard that this was the start of civil war and even that Che Guevara had risen from the dead. The whole story of his death in Bolivia a few years before had been a political trick. In short, apart from sitting all day in silence on our mattresses, there was not much to do. Though I should add that at noon we took turns at the window to watch the Ambassador's lady swimming with her poodles in the pool in the garden.

The pea soup kept me awake as usual. On my trajectory toward the bathroom I stepped on someone by mistake.

The next day His Excellency the Ambassador, as a humanitarian gesture, had the servants' television set brought in, and we were able to watch an announcer, stiff and brilliantined, saying:

"The Chief of Staff of the Armed Forces has stated that the present state of internal war is not a juridical fiction but the realistic response of a people determined to survive."

We squatted like a cluster of toads on the floor, dragging our mattresses closer so that we could hear.

"The city of Viña del Mar is holding its fifteenth song festival. Participants will come from Greece, France, Italy, Mexico, Japan, Great Britain and other countries."

A beautiful, catlike young female then came on the screen to announce the return of American series like Mission Impossible, John Quest and Bonanza. After all this unexpected news the set developed difficulties and shortly went back for good to the servants' quarters.

Vargas organized a committee among the inmates, with a president, a secretary and a treasurer. Vargas himself was voted in as treasurer. We took up a collection to buy cigarettes and valium. We asked the majordomo if he could buy them for us on his day off, and he, with his usual kindness and his white gloves, agreed.

A bearded reporter stretched out quite horizontally on his mattress, never moving, exclaimed that he had lost forty kilos and was having trouble getting accustomed to his new body, which gave him the impression that if he moved he would be struck dead by the breathing of the other inhabitants of the room.

At times I would shut myself into the bathroom for a change of space, but this was difficult and not a very original idea as there was a psychologist couple who did the same thing when the spirit moved them. They would stay there a most inappropriate length of time, and we could hear smothered laughter and suspicious sound effects. The rest of us, waiting in the next room, would maintain the most absolute silence on these occasions, as if it were really worthwhile imagining all kinds of emotions forbidden in such circumstances. On this day the Spaniard told us that he spent two years lost and wandering in the mountains during the Civil War, eating roots and acorns. Juan de la Capilla made a present of the Chilean flag to Vargas, and every night afterwards Vargas slept in it, wrapped up like a baby.

As we were having dinner we knew that on the ground floor of the Residence the new minister of Health was guest of honour of our ambassadors. This we learned from the majordomo, who asked us to keep the strictest silence, as if we did not even exist. On this occasion he did not leave the wine-glasses on our beds, but brought only water glasses — a pleasant surprise, because keeping so many dishes on the edge of a mattress is most inconvenient, and all that expensive china and Czech crystal makes you nervous. Especially just to eat a ladleful of thin soup and nothing more. We could hear helicopters searching for clandestine groups in the dark, as usual, and the majordomo, for a change, took away our dishes on an elegant silver-plated tray.

The following night there was a tremor. Chile is a land of earthquakes, and nothing could have been more normal. We all ran down the marble stairs. Two crystal chandeliers were shaken to bits. For the first time we set foot on the carpets of the Embassy drawing room. It was an enormous room with bright green armchairs, and windows with velvet curtains. There was a splendid fireplace whose mantelpiece was cluttered with souvenirs of exotic places and family photos in gilt frames. I sat down on a brocade chair. Suddenly, screams and panic: the pregnant woman was sure she was going to give birth. The ambassadorial couple arrived in pyjamas, along with their poodles which were unusually friendly and went about licking everyone. In an unexpected burst of generosity the master of the house got out two bottles of whiskey, and the majordomo, impeccable and dauntless as ever, brought still more glasses of Czech crystal and poured an elegant and adequate serving for everybody. Somebody put on a record. Vargas and the ambassador's lady, who was less inhibited than usual, danced a tango. People made bets about her age, judging by her legs which you could see when she took long steps, and which, it was obvious, were still vigorous and supple, inspiring all sorts of mischievous smiles among the men in their underwear and blankets.

The Spaniard took advantage of the occasion to relate

that he was a baker. The reporter with the black beard, who had come downstairs with the help of two of us, said 2,200 American citizens had come in as tourists before the coup d'état. He said there was a travel agency that specialized in promoting exciting excursions for Americans in search of danger. It also paid their tickets and expenses. It was called the CIA-Inn. At the same time, he remarked, relations with that country were almost completely cut off at this moment. The furious Spaniard, with extravagant rage, insulted the defunct president, might he rest in peace, saying that he had been an imbecile, giving up one ministry after the other to the generals, allowing the government to crumble bit by bit like Largo Caballero during the Spanish republic.

The bearded reporter went on citing figures about military aid from Uncle Sam to Chile during the present year, saying it had been as high as fifteen million dollars, while the estimated national budget of the preceding years had normally been less than a million. Then he fainted, from sheer weakness. The majordomo revived him with two scrambled eggs, served in high style.

The inquisitive little girl held an exhibition of her childish sketches, in which there appeared many soldiers on horseback, mingled with cats, dogs and poor people. Also the Virgin and certain angels of the Guard armed with rocks and *marraqueta* buns.

Juan de la Capilla went to pieces completely; the whiskey came out of his eyes as enormous tears, and then he showed everyone his fiancée's picture. The inquisitive little girl said:

"What? Priests getting married!"

Finally, the Spaniard wound up the evening saying that Baudelaire had been the son of a sacristan.

I don't know how many days we spent waiting in the room, sitting on our mattresses, our bodies silent. Taking valium, playing cards or dominoes.

Through the window one afternoon we saw the Ambassador playing tennis with the minister of Health, a man with a face like a bulldog, dressed in green. As background music we could hear a recording of Lili Marlene in German. This led us to all manner of suspicions.

The good-natured fat woman said all the Chilean military were descendants of Nazi immigrants and she also said something about Prussian helmets.

The bearded reporter exclaimed that there were no arms, and I thought of the machine guns I had, buried under the rosebushes in the garden of my house, and I thought of my wife and my son.

Juan de la Capilla read the Bible — the passage where Jesus drives the money-changers out of the temple with whips, and explained that this was the first revolutionary action in history, for the whips were the arms they had available.

The Spaniard stood up, took the floor, talking like a derailed locomotive:

"Revolutions are made with guns, with stones, with sticks, with slingshots. We had three years of civil war. Then came the International Brigades. I took refuge in the Embassy of Chile. Pablo Neruda was the consul. He rented three houses. Then Neruda shipped us off to Valparaiso in a boat called the Winnipeg...."

Vargas screamed:

"Let's get out of here! Let's go! We're a bunch of cowards. We'll all end up crazy like this wandering Spaniard here!"

Vargas went up to the Spaniard and punched him once in the stomach. The old man fell down like a wounded dog.

Vargas wanted to hit him again, but the majordomo came in with the dogs who had just had their swimming lesson and shook themselves all over us with great delight. He had brought us the cigarettes and valium we had ordered. We held a meeting. Cigarettes and valium were handed out and we sank back into our usual silence.

What was our surprise when, one day not long after, we received a visit from his Excellency, elegant as ever in his dark pin-stripe. He made the following speech to us:

"It is possible that the reasons you had for seeking asylum no longer exist. Fear sometimes forces us to make decisions that we later regret. Those who wish to go home will be accompanied by an embassy employee. We have kept your identities a total secret."

Everyone remained still, looking around the assembled faces, dull-eyed, searching for a way out.

The Ambassador went on:

"Nobody speaks up? In that case we shall try to obtain a safe-conduct authorizing you to leave the country."

He retired solemnly from the room. We lay down again. The magic effects of the soup were with us, as always. The pregnant woman cried:

"Please, open the window, I'm sick..."

Next morning when we awoke we discovered that the Spaniard had tried to run away the previous evening and had been killed by a rifle shot — some neighbour, no doubt. The dogs had discovered his body floating in the pool.

This news affected everyone. First of all, the Ambassador and his wife, who had to dispose of the corpse in a flour sack (poor baker, who'd have believed it!). They had it transported outside the city and thrown into a distant sand pit. As for the rest of us, the event made us melancholy, apathetic and more silent than ever.

João, however, let go with transcendental phrases from time to time, such as:

"Every revolutionary process has its setbacks."

The bearded reporter put in his two cents' worth from his fakir's bed in a thin, exhausted voice:

"The first year of our exile we'll make the big headlines. Then we'll turn up in the second section, and as the years go by each day our story will get smaller, less important."

Despite such conversations I myself felt lively, hungry and filled with hope, and lucky to find myself conforming to the medico-legal definition of being alive.

How many days did we spend this way? I believe thirty. What I do remember is the night John John dropped in to tell us to get our clothes together, we were going to the airport next day on our way to the Land of the Other Extreme. I slept with my pants under the mattress to press them.

We got up early and around ten o'clock we were taken to the airport. The usual electoral posters and childish murals from the time of the former government had been covered with white paint. The city looked clean and orderly. It seemed impossible that such a radical change had taken place in the country. The mountains were there, beautiful as a Swiss postcard. Not many people on the sidewalk. We arrived at an airport building of corrugated metal, with fragile, temporary hangars. It was crowded with people about to leave forever. We got into a long lineup for the security check which was to see if we were carrying arms or metal blades or other subversive objects. In the lineup I saw Cooper, a colleague. We did not exchange greetings. He winked at me, as if to say we should pretend not to know each other.

When the check was over our safe-conducts and flight tickets were verified. We made our farewells. A mutual pat on the back with John John. I shook his hand and thanked him for our stay in the Ambassador's most agreeable house. We climbed in single file into the plane. A Caravelle. Cooper was in the seat next to mine. What a surprise! We embraced. I gave him a sketchy account of our life in the embassy.

"And what about you?" I asked.

He replied with a little smile.

"Me? I have a British passport."

Cooper, Cooper, of course!

"My grandfather was English. The whole gang of us were registered at the Consulate."

I laughed. I hadn't made out too badly either, and I didn't have a British passport. I didn't have any passport, but I'd been lucky. Being alive. Getting out of prison. And now I was on my way, so easily. With a safe-conduct, in this Caravelle! A blonde woman came along and offered me gum. I took it. You could hear background music, and the smooth voice of the blonde or another one like her saying we should fasten our seat-belts. The first thing I'd do at the next stop would be to send a postcard to Sara and the kid. And to Lucia. To Lucia as well. Absorbed in my thoughts, hearing the soft blues on the loudspeaker, I hardly knew when it happened, but two men in grey were standing in front of me.

"Antonio Rojas," they said, roughly, "You're under arrest."

I couldn't get it out, couldn't say no, it can't be, there's a mistake, then they took me by force and pushed me down the steps of the plane. I found myself on the way back to the city in a bus filled with prisoners. All I could see through the small window was the Caravelle taking off with its passengers. It was heading for the clouds, and I — I was here alone, here in the other extreme, wiped out, forever.

How Are You?

WE'RE BOTH refugees. Neither of us has a passport. Our coats were both rescued from the garbage. We're trying to adapt. Casimir was sponsored by a Jewish group looking for a tax write-off. I, by a committee of former priests who had lived in Latin America. He was given a TV set and a black suit. I got a mattress complete with bedbugs. He talks about synagogues, I talk about the priests and their committee. We have something in common. Something that oozes out of our pores: a touch of scepticism, a vestige of bitterness.

We met at language class. An inadvertant glance and some words about the weather. Seven months of snow. The freezing, cutting wind.

"And the people here, they're so simple-minded, they're interested in nothing and nobody, they just don't want their lives complicated . . . ."

He is tall, blond and blue-eyed, with an aquiline nose — the face of a movie actor. But there's something more about it, a certain interesting hardness. I'm short, thin and pale, with black, curly hair. Seen together, we're nothing but contrasts.

Our subway car was late. I asked Casimir:

"What's the matter?"

A man in a beige raincoat answered with the indifference so common here:

"They're cleaning up the blood."

Perhaps it all happened because we realized at the same time, from that chilling remark, that in the next station there had been another suicide.

"That's February for you," said Casimir.

We got off at Berri and took the Longueuil subway line. There we changed to a bus full of Greeks, Pakistanis, Arabs, Portuguese and I don't know what else, all blue as mulberries from the cold. They pay us forty-five dollars a week for going to these courses and learning English. He said he came from Lodz. I'm from Valparaiso. He left Poland because he is a Jew. I told him about the military putsch.

The learning system is simple but effective. The teacher says, "How are you?" and we repeat it after him, taking turns, just like real schoolchildren but grown tall or bearded or fat or depressed. The first day he said "How are you" about a hundred times until I was dizzy. Not counting how often I heard it from our side. Casimir winked at me and tapped his temple with a finger. He was going crazy too. I smiled at him across the room. Twenty weeks of this just to get money for the rent.

There's a half-hour break for lunch. No more How-are-you's for a while. But we hear the deafening noise of coca cola and soup machines in the large cafeteria. Casimir and I sit down with the five thousand other immigrant pupils in this language school. Each one has his little packed lunch, "ethnic" lunches, rice or shishkebab, goulash or meat pie, pasta or marzipan. Wrapped in aluminum foil or plastic bags. Neither of us had ever tried soup from a machine before, or coffee that tasted like gasoline.

"I think I have a fever," I told him.

"It's the language course," he said. "It's as if they erased your power of reason, the way you wipe out a tape when you record on top of the message."

It's funny how a clever remark, coming from an attractive person, seems even more convincing. And when the conversation is in a new language, you feel as if you're rediscovering words. In that moment we looked at each other as if we belonged. Two lonely people who have found someone at last, to their surprise. He asked me if I had any family. One sister and my father, I replied. He was an only son, and his widowed mother was still in Poland.

A strident bell put an end to the break, and the cafeteria emptied. The garbage containers were stuffed with papers and wrappers. Crumbs and overflowing ashtrays littered the tables. The afternoon was the same as the morning, with its How-are-you's.

We went back together in the subway. He lives on St. Lawrence Boulevard, near Waldman's, half a block from the Portuguese store where they pluck the chickens live before the customer's eyes. That's where he buys the chicken feet and necks to make his Jewish barley soup. He's also just a stone's throw from Four Brothers and Warshaw's supermarkets, and cheese stores and all those little ethnic shops that sell unusual products at cheap prices.

I live on Van Horne near the post office, the supermarket, the drug store, the bank and the bus-stop. I keep telling myself it's not such a bad neighbourhood.

Casimir rents a room above a delicatessen that sells bagels and cream cheese and smoked-meat sandwiches. I, oddly enough, live above a pizzeria. That explains why my building is infested with cockroaches. Sometimes at night when I go in the bathroom I see them running in the tub or the wash-basin. These cockroaches are pale, long and yellowish, not like the Chilean ones which are black and round.

"Are Polish cockroaches different?" I asked him.

"Perhaps," he replied.

He says that there are lots of them in his kitchen. They are actually frightening at times. The exterminator who came there two weeks ago told him each cockroach lays eighty eggs, and the eggs take twenty-eight days to turn into active creatures with legs. His landlord is stingy and saves oil by turning down the heat. Like Casimir, he is a Polish Jew, one of the community. I'm lucky by comparison. I can't say that my house is freezing. On the contrary, I almost suffocate in the stifling heat. I live on the fourth floor, and there's an elevator. That gives a little class to the building. The elevator locks, and there's a different key for each floor. The landlady, a Greek dressmaker with a blond wig, lives across from me. At times I pay her an angry visit, trying with gestures to make her understand that somebody forgot to shut the inside grill of the lift and I've had to climb the hundred and twenty-two steps, exhausted. Another small but mysterious detail about this elevator: every Monday some unidentified tenant with idle hands draws a gigantic male sex in coloured chalk on its wall. The Greek woman's son comes home drunk and discovers the drawing, and never fails to hammer on every door in a vain attempt to find the guilty artist.

"Not easy to get to sleep, Casimir!"

Every day the trip from Berri to Longueuil, from Longueuil to La Prairie. One class after the other, with Casimir. We get to know other students. A Bulgarian ballet dancer who escaped from a plane during its landing in Ghent; Mahmala, a Lebanese industrialist who despises the rest of us; three Haitians, refugees from Duvalier; a Greek worker; a quiet Portuguese girl who works nights; Alberto, a Colombian schoolteacher; and the professor, a Hindu, a coffee-coloured ringer for an upper-class Englishman. Altogether there are twelve human beings in this overheated room where we can see snow through the window and the distant white horizon. We sit very close to each other, Casimir and I. Sometimes I look at him, sometimes he looks my way. He often sighs deeply and rolls his eyes toward the ceiling, showing his impatience.

On Mondays we usually start the class with the sentence, "What did you do during the weekend?" We hear Mahmala recount in broken English how his wife bathed him on Saturday night. Lakis, the Greek, is a night watchman for Canadian National Railways. The Portuguese girl's name is Ilda, she lives with her mother and seven sisters. The Colombian arrived in Canada with his whole family and the maid and is trying to scrape together the money for a house. I don't talk much. Casimir says he's the only Jew who eats herring seven days a week. Oh yes, I forgot to mention Félix, a Spaniard and formerly a priest. He was a late starter in the course. He's trying desperately to make up for his years of abstinence. He makes his approach to the girls in the class on the slimmest pretext — apparently without success. After each failed attempt he laughs to himself, glassy-eyed and happy, his mind filled with what might have been.

During breaks we talk to each other. Almost always it's about some bad news from one of our countries. Murders, military coups, sometimes wars, new economic crises or exotic disasters like floods, earthquakes, hurricanes or unexpected droughts.

At noon Casimir and I go for walks. He says Siberia isn't as cold as Montreal. I had never seen snow, and I can't get used to the stalactites hanging from the moustaches of people with colds. He's used to the cold in Poland. He shows me how to wear my scarf and toque and gloves, and explains how I mustn't press my nose against store windows. It might stick and I'd go away with open nostrils like a skull. Casimir says the cold acts as a local anesthetic. You feel nothing, but your cartilage is solidifying, your ears can fall off and silently sink into the snow. For me so many things are new: being careful on the slippery sidewalks, with my heavy coat and big boots. Here everything is provided for, he says. If you slip and break a bone you can sue the city for not clearing the way in time. That's nice to know. Some people get pensions. The ones who unthinkingly and involuntarily were hurt this way and can't work. Night and day the snow removal goes on, with blowers that from time to time suck in a pedestrian.

"People have to be very careful about their children," Casimir explained.

The other students don't attract much of our attention. They are shy and introverted and monotonously repeat anything they are told. Their weekend activities are also not very exciting. Shopping, washing clothes, cooking, watching TV (for those who have one). We listen to detailed descriptions of their apartments, the nearby park, the stores where they shop, and the buses they take to come to the school.

We eat together, and very quickly. It's always an egg sandwich that we've made at home. In the few minutes left we go skating. We've bought used skates for fifty cents, from a Jewish shoemaker Casimir knew about, on St. Lawrence. Casimir was a champion skater on the frozen rivers of Poland. I can barely stay on my feet. He helps by taking my arm. From time to time he lets me go and turns to look at me, his frosted breath steaming out of his mouth. We don't talk during these times. The silence is comfortable, almost intimate. Sometimes he re-arranges my scarf, and I let him do it. I wait for these small, familiar gestures, observing his handsome face, saying nothing, as if something secret had made a delicate landing between us.

After class we take the subway together. We go for a coffee at a restaurant in one of the stations. He has all kinds of strategies for living cheaply. He buys leftover fish and greens, and old cheese. He checks out the garbage cans of food stores. He steals his electricity from the hydro line in the street with a special device he made himself. He even has a stove that was donated by his Jewish association. When we go our separate ways we kiss each other on both cheeks. He gives me a hug, and holds me a second or two longer than necessary. Just imperceptibly: I notice it but no one else would.

Perhaps it was our previous education that brought us closer. That's what I think now when I try to find what lay behind our relationship. He had studied economics, and I was in social sciences. We feel that we're the educated ones in the class. We're the ones that speak English best. The language of success, of work, of the opportunity everyone came here in search of. Many of the other pupils hang around us to improve or practise the little they have mastered. This gives us a certain feeling of power in the school for immigrants. Sometimes the texts we have to repeat start with phrases like "Try me!" or "Give me a chance!" I suppose it's to stimulate our ambition. And we also make up written dialogues. We're divided up in groups according to our level, and Casimir and I always end up together. We write stories as if they were for a real play. He is a Strindberg fan, I like Ibsen. He talks about Grotowski, I about Polanski. He's a bit like Polanski. Something about his manner. . . . Not long ago we did a parody of Romeo and Juliet. We rehearsed it in a café, and when we parted he kissed me on the lips. I tried to avoid it, I was afraid, I had a sense of foreboding. He seemed surprised at himself. Later he called me up and tried to explain. I went to sleep unconcerned, thinking of his nice-boy face.

Class after class, break after break, glance after glance, the weeks went past. The course was coming to an end. The teacher, always enthusiastic about life in Canada, showed us films like "The Story of a Lumberman," "The Life of a Tractor Driver," or "The Weekend of a Worker on the Snow Removal Team." All the films were optimistic, and dealt with the joys of productive labour. He taught us songs like "Jingle Bells" which we sang off key in a smiling chorus, each with his indigenous accent. Above all, he taught us to fill out forms and make phone calls in our search for work. Work? Had it come to that! Work. The word provoked anxious frowns and long faces.

"Marcia, let's leave together," Casimir said during the break.

So we took the bus together to Longueuil station, with its shops and lottery stand. I was going to pay my fare, but he said:

"No, no, I'm paying."

But we didn't move. We stood waiting in front of the turnstile as the crowd went by. Suddenly he exclaimed:

"Did you see that?"

The machines had rejected two subway tickets.

"I always have to wait, but I eventually get through free."

Penny-pinching, saving a bit here, a bit there — I hated it. He was Jewish through and through. In the subway he said:

"I've been wanting to invite you for so long. I've got some

really good soup, wait till you see. Leftovers — that's my specialty!"

I thought it over for a moment, then started laughing. Was I going to refuse my first invitation in this town?

His apartment was small. One room, with a distinct atmosphere. He shared a bathroom and toilet with the owner. We ate some smoked herring and soup. Leftovers or not, it wasn't too bad. We had some wine and I felt a little tipsy. The place was empty, with no decorations on its white walls. There were no chairs, and we had to sit on the edge of the bed. He asked me about the military putsch. He couldn't get into his head that such a thing had happened. Such an exemplary country, so unique. I explained the usual things about multi-nationals and imperialism. A small, poor country hasn't the right to make its own decisions. He told me about Poland. For centuries it had been divided, dismembered, invaded. For a time it had been wiped right off the map. He became aggressive, saying that socialism wasn't worth the trouble, it led to a paranoid daily life and the new ruling class of bureaucrats. I was sick of the whole discussion. But he went on:

"The multi-nationals are one thing, but on the other hand you simply copied our mistakes."

He stopped and came near me, kissed my right hand.

I drew back a little, thinking of other things.

"It's been months and months since I had anybody near me. Come and lie down beside me for a minute."

"No!" I said, apprehensive.

"Why should we deny ourselves a few moments of tenderness?"

His eyes were like crystal.

He cuddled close to my shoulder.

"It's snowing," he said.

He held my face and said very slowly:

"You're beautiful!"

I said nothing. I floated in the moment, imagining the snow and the freezing wind outside, thinking about the two of us there on the edge of the bed, refugees for opposite reasons. I wanted to run away, but we kissed interminably, mingling our despairs and solitudes. I was trembling.

"What's the matter?" Casimir asked, stroking my hair.

I was weeping softly. He repeated,

"Come, please?"

I almost gave in, but I was overcome by a terrible sadness. I gathered my courage and whispered:

"I can't."

He put out the light. We undressed, little by little. Awkwardly, we embraced. Suddenly I pulled back and, in spite of myself, told him how I had been arrested.

"I was in a police station," I said. "Two policemen beat me..."

He switched on the lamp again. Through my tears I saw Casimir, naked, and realized that he had great scars on one shoulder and arm. And he discovered the marks on my breast and back.

"This too?" he asked, pointing to the burn mark on my breast.

I nodded and closed my eyes for a moment. I didn't want to talk, I didn't want to remember. Then I opened them, and saw his grave face. His blond hair was tousled. His expression was hard and tragic.

"I'll tell you a secret," he said softly, playing with my fingers. Was he afraid someone would hear him?

"I'm not Jewish."

He paused for a second, then went on in the same hushed voice:

"I had to learn Yiddish and go to the synagogue. I got these marks trying to escape from prison." He showed me his arm. "For years I tried to get out of Poland. At last I discovered an organization that helped Jews leave the country. I spent seven years telling lies, appearing before one tribunal after another. I swore my mother had a Jewish lover during the time of the Nazis. I went around with a cyanide pill in my pocket, just in case they...."

We were both melancholy now. He was frowning, his eyes half-closed. Nervously, he took my hand. He ran a finger over my face, shyly, barely touching. He kissed me on the cheek. We held each other tight, searching for more marks of pain and violence on the other's body.

He turned off the light again, and the darkness drove us under the covers. We kissed in silence, side by side, together and alone, two prisoners in a single trap.

The next day was Saturday. We woke early. Casimir made coffee, and said in his usual tone:

"What are you going to do next week when the course ends? How will you pay the rent?"

"I don't know. Work in a factory. Or a restaurant."

"You're young, you're pretty, forget about building socialism, I know some businessmen in their fifties, they'd be delighted to marry you. The Town of Mount Royal is a good neighbourhood, people with money and Cadillacs and big houses. Maybe money doesn't make you happy, but it helps. I'll introduce you to some of them."

I laughed, but it must have looked more like a grimace.

"Are you crazy?"

"Crazy? I'm just fed up with being a candidate for living, I'm fed up being poor. Hanging around with people that are run-of-the-mill mediocrities. I want dough. Whatever I have to do for it."

I looked at him attentively. He was excited.

"I'm going to Toronto," he added. "There's nothing doing here. The political situation is too unstable. Quebec's going to be a big problem."

He went over to his bed and took out a shoe-box from beneath it. He removed the lid and showed me what was inside: the photo of a very ugly woman. He paused for a moment to see my reaction, then exclaimed:

"I'm going to marry her!"

After a second he went on:

"Her father owns a factory."

I was aghast.

"You never told me!"

"It was through the synagogue, " he said.

And he offered me a second cup of coffee, saying:

"So there's an end to romance. I'd like to believe in it, but...."

I didn't want coffee. I put on my overcoat, my boots, my scarf and my toque.

"Hey, we're going skating Monday, aren't we?"

I nodded. As I crossed the threshold I saw some enormous cockroaches, yellowish like mine. The only thing we have in common, I thought. The exhaust from the buses soiled the snow, turned it beige or even coffee-coloured. People bent over forward to escape the bitter wind.

That Monday Casimir didn't come to the course. I phoned him at home but there was no answer. Then the course was over.

A month later I got a card from him. From Toronto. It said, "Married and manager." Then came a few details of his plans: "When I get my citizenship I'm changing my name again. Casimir Davis or better Henry Davis. There's a lot of prejudice against Jews here. I'll be able to visit Poland and see

my mother. And some day I'll be a wheel on Wall Street."
Below, in capitals, he added:

HOW ARE YOU?

I re-read the card with care. No, there was no return address.

The Vietnamese Hats

AT FIRST we used to talk from one window to the next, asking names and so on. We'd tell each other how we came to be arrested and what they had asked about in the interrogation. And we listened to the screams that came and went through the bars. The soldiers kicked at our doors to make us shut up, or blew their whistles. We used to sing, too, anything at all, from nursery songs to the Internationale.

There were eighteen of us packed into a cell for four. The walls were adobe, with a dirt floor. On one side, the massive metal door, always closed. On the other side, the bars of the small, high window that looked out on the central courtyard of the prison.

There was a flap at the bottom of the door. Mornings and evenings the guards pushed a few trays through it carrying a loathsome soup made of noodles and cracklings. We ate it. There was nothing to drink but powdered milk. They took us out to the toilets for five minutes, along with twelve hundred others. The public prison of Rancagua had been evacuated to take us in as prisoners of war. There were thirty toilets, the square kind, for squatting, with raised places for the feet and a hole in the middle. There were no doors, and the bowls were full of excrement. While one of us squatted with pants down the others lined up making gestures to hurry up, staring, laughing and telling filthy jokes. I couldn't shit like that. I could barely pee. I washed the filth off my feet and went away without relief.

During the day we paced the cell or did exercises to relax. We played X's and O's, scratching on the wall with slivers.

The nights were cold. We laid our coats on the floor. Despite the body heat from the others, I could feel the cold earth behind me. There were some bunks on one side which had been taken apart. Some of us slept lying down, others sitting. Every four hours we traded positions. By the end of the day the place stank, especially when the plastic bags were filled with urine and shit. We had improvised this solution and soon it became standard procedure. Two kind guards gave us the plastic bags without the soldiers' knowledge. To take full advantage of the system we used them one at a time until each in turn was full. Shitting and hoping — that was all we could do. Go through the contortions of opening the bag, squatting at the same time with pants down, taking care not to make a false move that would splash the excrement on the floor. I felt immersed in a sticky filth that stuck to my skin. Grease. I dreamed I was eating some tasty-looking wieners filled with shit and vomit. When the place grew quiet and the sound of heavy boots in the corridors grew distant, we would throw the plastic bags out the window. Next day the soldiers would shout and want to know who had done it. The bags burst and scattered the turds all over the yard. They forced a few people from their cells to clean up the mess. After a month of this they began taking us to the toilets in smaller groups, half an hour for each group. We had time to take a shower and wash some of our clothes. There was no soap, but it was refreshing to stand under the shower. Some of the dirt in our clothing came out if it was scrubbed with a little earth on the edge of the stone cistern.

They hired a photographer. A skinny guy with a moustache wearing a black suit, who took pictures of all twelve hundred of us, front and side view. Our beards had all grown, our shirts showed sweat-marks, our hair was long and dirty and clung to our skulls with the accumulated grease of our stay in that place. We would be immortal in some archive looking like real criminals.

I began to despair, penned and crammed in as we were. I hated the others. I could have killed them all. Wiped them out. Made their smelly bodies disappear. The tiniest, imperceptible movement of another prisoner's arm made me aggressive. Furiously, with a kind of anger I never normally felt, I would strike out at the person who had touched me. Or I hurled myself at the wall, trying to knock myself out. Sometimes we would get into brutal fights, and the others would try to calm the antagonists. Ljubetic would say to me:

"Come on, Slim, take it easy."

A guy in a grey sweater let me have one in the eye. I bled so badly they took me to the infirmary. It was a small, green room and the attendant also wore green. There were four beds, but the injured were also lying on the floor. Some were unable to move. I asked them why. Nobody answered. There was a sepulchral silence in the place. Two days later I was taken back to the cell.

* * *

It must have been around nine in the morning when they

called out the first twenty-five prisoners to be interrogated. The names were shouted over loud-speakers. Those mentioned had to identify themselves by replying with their cell numbers. We were number sixty. None of us was called this time. The twenty-five never came back. We asked from window to window what had happened. We heard:

"No, no, So-and-so never came back last night. They didn't bring him back."

We were very worried. A guard kicked at the door, shouting:

"Of course they came back. They're in the infirmary."

Suddenly I understood the silence in the infirmary. In our cell an oppressive anxiety set in. Six days in a row they called out twenty-five people who never came back. Demoralized, we waited for our turn. On the sixth day we heard that they were coming back toothless, bruised and injured. Ljubetic and El Polilla looked at me. Ljubetic was tall, with black hair and clear blue eyes. His father was a Yugoslav from Magallanes. We didn't say a word. The Vietnamese hats were our great obsession. I wondered which of us three would be interrogated first. We mustn't soften up under torture, that was clear. I was afraid about El Polilla, he was so young and nervous. Eighteen at the most. I couldn't sleep. I had been a worker in a canning factory. At the last minute I had joined a group called "The Mad Bombers." The leader was a Brazilian with no toenails. His name was Wellington, and he was a chemical engineer who had been Marighella's bodyguard. When he pulled his shirt up in the back it looked as if he'd had smallpox, he had so many cigarette burns from being tortured in his own country. He always said we had to be prepared, he didn't want things to happen to us as they had to Joao Goulart.

One day Wellington said to me:

"I need some tin. I want to make some Vietnamese hats."

"What's that?" I wanted to know.

"That's the weapon they used in Vietnam to stop the Yankees' tanks."

"I don't have any tin," I said. "I get my cans ready-made."

He explained that he needed tin that was thin so that it bent easily. You had to cut a circle out of it and make a cone. The mixture of sulphur and gunpowder was held in the cone. Then you cut a smaller disc of tin to cover the opening of the cone, bending the edges like a tart-crust to make it hold.

"They're very powerful," he said.

"The government doesn't agree with making bombs," I said, terrified.

I hesitated a moment and went on:

"Maybe somebody could get you tin in Santiago. I don't dare ask the supervisor. But I'll see what I can do...."

Shortly afterwards I got involved in the scheme. I came across this cocky guy who used to go on about the permanent revolution and all that. He told me:

"No problem, comrade. I'll put some sheets of 2 x 4 among the jars, but don't let anybody know or I'll get fired."

That's how we got the sheets into the canning factory. A few of us took them and hid them in a storage cellar. The Brazilian shut himself up in the marmalade refrigerator-room and made the bombs. When they were made he and El Polilla took them up into the hills and buried them. I saw once that they had some that were twenty or thirty centimetres long or bigger. I told the Brazilian without mincing words:

"I get the material but that's all. I don't want to know any more. Not where you hide them, or anything else."

I'd been thinking about all that, and hadn't heard them calling El Polilla's name. Stunned, he answered:

"Number sixty!"

He stared at Ljubetic and then at me. I had imagined this moment often. Just as it happened. A guard opened the door and two soldiers took him away. I trembled the whole day long. Ljubetic was the legal officer of the company. He knew all about the hats. I wanted to go over to him but in another way I hesitated. There were so many of us packed in there. I didn't dare whisper. There might be a stool-pigeon in the cell.

Next morning we heard from the other windows that El Polilla had been going toward the infirmary with his ears half torn-off. I was in a mad fury, and started kicking the door. I didn't say a word all day. They brought us a sort of dumpling soup. I felt useless, small, crushed. Good for nothing but waiting. And waiting for what? For them to knock out my teeth, tear off my fingernails, rip out my hair. My brain was working overtime. Stop, stop turning around in my fucking head, will you? I lay down but couldn't keep my eyes shut. I felt as if they were bulging out of my head. My right eye was twitching out of control. I touched it to see if this was really happening or if I was going mad. The minutes went by. I had to make the most of my four hours lying down. The tension held. My jaws ached.

El Polilla came back to the cell bruised black and blue, his shirt in shreds. He wouldn't talk much. So they took him up into the hills. He showed them a place where he had camped with Wellington. He told them he'd wanted to go off to Argentina with some friends. The soldiers didn't believe him, and started tearing out underbrush, lifting boulders and digging holes. But they found nothing. Then they'd brought him back, beat the shit out of him and left him in the infirmary.

* * *

At the end of the second month they let us out into the open air. The yard was a long rectangle with prefabricated structures in the middle called *carretas*. In normal times the regular prisoners got together in groups to prepare their meals. We did the same. There were oil cookers, and the food was sent by international organizations. There were neither chairs nor tables. We sat on the ground to eat, and stared at each other.

A young man came back from interrogation with a fractured skull. The mayor of Rancagua heard about it and was furious. He forced the officers in charge to transfer the prisoner to a hospital. He wrote a letter to the prison governor saying that he would not stand for any more torture within his city's jurisdiction. He went on a hunger strike, all by himself. He took up his post in front of the prison gate and didn't move for seven days. His wife brought him water. We took up a collection for him, a bit of small change, and got one of the more sympathetic guards to buy the present. A modest copper plate, on which we had engraved: "To the mayor of the city of Rancagua, for his defence of human rights. A souvenir from the prisoners of war."

The mayor was fired from his position. We organized a farewell ceremony in the yard. The military, who couldn't oppose this, went along with it hypocritically. They brought in a band. Forty or so men in dress uniforms. They played the national anthem. We decided that nobody should sing it, except the verse that says something about an "asylum against oppression." We shouted like madmen for half an hour, repeating the phrase like a scratched record. Then they broke up the party with their rifle butts and we were returned to our cells.

At three in the morning they took Ljubetic out for interrogation. This surprised me: at that time of day the Military Prosecutor's office was closed. It occurred to me, and the idea refused to go away, that El Polilla had talked. And Wellington — where was he? El Polilla was asleep. I wanted to wake him up, but couldn't manage it. It was cold in the cell and I hated to move. I was sitting up. Though all those individuals were around me I had the impression they were non-existent. They were dismembered slices of life. Piled side by side. I moved away from them. I thought of their faces as chunks of sticky flesh. At around six-thirty Ljubetic came back. He was crying, his nerves were shot. He grabbed the bars of the window and uttered inhuman cries, shouting:

"Rotten bastards!"

He laid his head on my shoulder, like a child. I wanted to ask him what had happened but didn't dare. It was strange to see this man, young and strong as he was, weeping and sobbing.

"One of these days we'll get even with all these killers," I told him.

He wasn't listening to me. He cried until we went out to the yard. There he sat down at one end of the carreta and was silent. He remained speechless for several weeks.

* * *

Three psychologists who had been arrested at the El Teniente mine turned up in our prison. They were pleasant fellows who always stuck together and went about trying to raise our morale. They went from one group to another in the yard, saying things like:

"Look, comrades, it's crazy being shut in like this. There are too many of us prisoners with not enough room. This makes us easy game for police informers. Let's do something! What can you do, comrade? Sing? Dance? Recite?"

And they got a singing contest going. We had to laugh, hearing our off-key, reedy voices. We improvised a little stage with chairs and scraps of board.

"Hey! We've got rags here!" said one of the psychologists. "Off with the old shirts, guys, we're going to make a football."

Some tore off their sleeves, others gave up their underwear shorts or a strip of towel or an old sock. At certain times we'd clear the yard and play soccer. That was less boring than seeing the whole twelve hundred of us walking around the place, it was enough to give you claustrophobia, seeing their faces and their wounds and bruises and everybody telling the same stories all the time.

We formed a group which improvised songs, as well as a choir and a puppet theatre. It was like a real fiesta. They took the psychologists away then and put them in solitary. But we kept up our activities with clandestine leaders. We even organized ourselves into political parties.

* * *

My memory is hazy about the first time they took me to interrogation. I know I'd been expecting it every day. And I know it happened a few weeks after they worked Ljubetic over. I got my call in the morning, The military offices were in the City Hall building. We left by the prison door with our hands behind our heads. A lot of women were waiting outside. Suddenly I saw Carmen. I barely nodded at her. She shouted:

"Oh Slim, you're alive!"

And she started crying. Then she continued:

"I've been coming every day since they took you. Nobody would tell me anything."

I looked at her. I'd have liked to go near her...

"Where are you going?" she asked.

I wanted to tell her they were going to torture me, beat the shit out of me for the Vietnamese hats, but I held back and gave her a vague answer. One of the guards gave me a kick in the ass and I moved on in single file. We crossed the square. The trees were beautiful and shining in the morning light. The City Hall was a shabby, old wooden building with two courtyards. They made us march still in single file, into the first one. We waited there sitting on the ground, with our hands up, surrounded by soldiers with machine guns. They rounded us up and located us near the torture room so that we could hear the cries and blows. The cries were heart-rending. We often heard the same words:

"For god's sake, kill me!"

Or:

"Leave me alone, can't you?"

They called us in one after the other, and each of us was kept about an hour inside. The cries grew fainter as the hour drew to an end, and sounded far away and feeble. And you could hear a thud on the floor, as if a sack of potatoes had fallen. Then they were kicked out half-naked and bleeding into the courtyard. Sometimes the victim was ordered to stand with those of us still waiting, sometimes he was left on the ground covered with blood. I was terrified. Seeing men come out toothless, their mouths torn, their lips swollen, and the rest of us waiting, sitting on the ground with our hands up, with nothing to eat or drink and nowhere to piss. I was afraid when my turn came I wouldn't be able to hold out. Before I even got into the room I imagined myself cracking. A nervous kind of horror possessed me.

When my turn came I was calmer. They blindfolded me and took me inside. A few blows and I was lying on the floor. The blows were somehow wet. Afterwards I realized they had used wet, rolled-up paper or sacks. That didn't leave so many marks. They shouted:

"You won't talk the easy way, eh? Well! Let's try the hard way!"

At the start I tried not to cry. I was hurting, and it seemed it would never stop. They asked about Plan Z, and I had no idea what it was, but they kept repeating:

"What was your connection with Plan Z?"

I didn't answer. And they shouted:

"Answer, you fucker!"

I still said nothing. I was slowly growing weaker. They crushed one of my eyes. It hurt badly. They hit me with a rubber truncheon on the head several times. They also gave me karate blows. And electric shocks in the mouth and on the testicles. I fainted. They turned off the current, gave me some water to drink and started the beatings again. I remember screaming in a sort of muffled voice. Several times. I was so tired. I could feel that I was losing blood in a number of places. I could barely think straight. I just waited for the next blow, and the next, and the next. I was nauseated. Bewildered. Two men hauled me out to the courtyard and took off the blindfold. I was thirsty. Everything looked blurred. I could scarcely hear my own voice asking:

"Water... please..."

One of the men waiting in the lineup came over and wiped the blood from my face with his shirt. His gesture was a swift one. I nodded my thanks to him, but a soldier kicked him in the back and knocked him down. He gave a hideous scream. They had broken his back. I fainted.

When I came to, the place was dark. It must have been about nine o'clock. They made us get up, and we walked slowly, as best we could, to the prison infirmary. There we spent the night. A peevish attendant looked after us. We ate some rice soup. After three days of medical care I was returned to the cell. I lay down, but couldn't sleep for fright. I was terrorized. I didn't want to take part in any of the activities. Not in singing, or plays, or soccer. I wondered if I'd be interrogated again. And I remembered my family. No work. Nothing to eat. They'd never recognize me if they saw me like this. I was so skinny my pants wouldn't stay up. I stank, with no shirt on. Stank of fever.

* * *

A few soldiers came into the courtyard, acting very friendly, setting up tables and chairs. Then they brought vases with flowers. And installed a TV set in one corner.

We asked them:

"What's the matter? Did the Junta fall?"

At first they wouldn't answer. Then one of them came over to us and explained.

"A commission's coming from the International Red Cross."

After a while two Frenchmen and two Swiss arrived. With them came about sixty officers, hemming them in on all sides, smiling pleasantly and speaking French. The officers came to where we were.

"Hey, you there! Tell us how you're treated here."

What could we say? We were well-treated. There were no problems. That we were organized in groups and the food was excellent. One Frenchman who looked like a sly priest said in a hard, almost military voice, in halting Spanish:

"If you don't mind, I would like to speak to these people alone, with none of the military around."

The officers looked at each other, and reluctantly, grumbling among themselves, retreated from the courtyard. When they were gone I showed the commission the bruises on my chest and others did likewise. We told them we were living like pigs here. That a plague of white lice had broken out in one of the cells. The guys were scratching their heads all day and the authorities wouldn't let them out for fear the things would spread. And about the tortured men in the infirmary, too.

"What? There's an infirmary here?" asked an innocent Swiss.

We had barely finished our tales when the sixty officers suddenly came back and the commission left. Then the soldiers took away the tables, chairs and flowers, and the TV set, and treated us to the usual knocks with their gun-butts.

* * *

One Thursday I was taken again to the interrogation building. They took me out of the prison, my hands behind my head, and again there were women around the gate. No one I knew. At the City Hall we waited in the second courtyard. This time we were guarded by ordinary soldiers. I talked with two of them, they came from Collaique. They were short, stout men. They said their nerves were shot. They couldn't stand it any more. We talked about food. They knew how to make curanto. They were half dead with hunger, but still obeyed orders. Like us, they didn't get enough to eat. My hands still held high, I awaited my turn, hearing the blows and screams as if I were inside. Somewhere in there I was going to keel over, I thought. As the day went by they called in the prisoners one after the other. Every time they tossed out a beaten body I shuddered. Then I grew used to the bruises, the blood and the stifled moans. I waited quietly, resigned, for my turn. My hands and feet were going to sleep from being so long in one position. I wanted to get it over with, once and for all. But they didn't torture me. I was taken back to my cell. I hated that cell. I couldn't bear contact with the others, the hunger, the stench, the depression. I hadn't eaten all day. Ljubetic gave me a glass of powdered milk and water left over from his lunch. I accepted, just to keep alive. I ended up sitting beside an old man of seventy — bleary-eyed, with a cataract on one side. I finally slept, exhausted. Next morning they called me out again. I was sure I wouldn't survive another day without food. I could hardly walk. At the gate I saw the same women as the previous day — plus one — waiting for news. Some of them were weeping. Carmen, for example. From a distance she waved.

"We're getting along all right!" she shouted.

Then, so far away, she showed me a package. It looked like clothing.

"When do you get out?" she asked.

How should I know? I felt as if this was the last day of my life. I looked at her but said nothing. I couldn't see her very well. I was near to collapsing. I managed to keep going. I forced my feet to move on the pavement, obstinately, pretending I was strong, to make her think I was well.

From the second courtyard I was the first to be taken inside. They put the blindfold over my eyes. They undressed me. I could hear three people walking around. They laid me on the floor. No insults this time. They attached electrical wires to my body. It moved of its own accord, and there was a frightful pain. In waves. Several times I bit my lips and tongue. I was screaming. And they went on chatting about what they were going to do on the weekend, as if nothing out-of-the-ordinary were happening. I wasn't able to follow what they said. I was listening to myself, continuously, and those outrageous screams of mine. How long this went on I don't know, but it was enough to break me. I wept to myself, and felt my split tongue bleeding. They stopped for a few minutes, then turned the current on again. This time I jumped convulsively and vomited. Green bile. Then they cut the current and everything was silent. I was thirsty. They removed the wires, and threw me half-dressed into the yard. I fell full-length on the pavement. I felt a sharp pain in my nose. I couldn't get up. I was there for hours and no one came near me. That night they took me to the infirmary. A doctor who happened by said I had a broken nose cartilage.

When I was returned to the cell a few days later I had a bandage on my head. And swelling all around my nose. My eyes were bloody and inflamed. It was a surprise to discover that El Polilla had been freed. Everybody was depressed. Somebody was crying. Some sat around in the yard, their tears simply flowing like a spring. Others were crying out of pure cowardice. They had to be bucked up with phrases like, "Come on, you're not going to be shot."

The plague of lice had spread. The prisoners were desperately scratching their heads and any other hairy places. People stayed away from each other as much as they could. I couldn't sleep for the bites. I don't know if I really had them — they were too small to see.

They brought us some paraffin oil to rinse our hair, and this helped for a while.

Ljubetic had turned silent. He was unapproachable.

Shocked, quite changed. His hair had turned partly white. A guard told me in confidence that his fiancée had been raped in front of him during his interrogation.

* * *

Eight months later they began releasing 15 men per day. An officer interrogated me. I confessed that I had been a party militant and had collaborated with the previous government because of my ideals. A week later they set me free, but in exile. Rancagua was to be my prison. They gave me a piece of paper stating that I was set free conditionally as there was no charge against me. And another paper I had to show every Wednesday at the police station nearest my domicile. And I was to go home at once. I had to observe the curfew. I had to read the official press and do what it said. I was forbidden to talk about the prison and the tortures. No meetings were to be held, either public or private. Political activity was suspended. I was supposed to help build Chile up again from the three years of chaos created by the last government.

It was strange to see Carmen again, and my father and the kid. They were thin. They kept asking me what happened to my nose. I didn't look too good. My eyes were bloodshot for a month. I was kicked out of the factory. I wasn't entitled to unemployment insurance. They wiped out my seniority.

I rested for a few days and started looking for work. For two weeks I picked plums out in the country. I planted tomatoes. I didn't earn much, I got a sack of potatoes and one of rice. Meat was out of the question. With the few pesos I earned I managed to buy a few eggs for my son, and some bread. Bread is filling.

I went to see a friend of the family, a man who worked for the government. I needed help. The place was plastered with posters saying: "Keep it brief, we have three wasted years to catch up on." I asked for the man. A guard wanted to see my papers. I told him:

"I'm a personal friend."

"Oh, just a minute..." and he went off and spoke to somebody in a nearby office.

They let me go through.

Erazo received me with eyes wide open in terror. He closed the door in a panic and whispered:

"What the devil are you doing here? You're crazy, coming here to see me!"

"I thought maybe you could help me to find a job."

He wrung his hands.

"You're mad, don't you know? You're on the black list. What if they'd asked for your card downstairs! You'd be double-blackballed!"

He paced up and down for a few seconds, then took a pencil and played with it nervously.

"I've had it up to here," he said. "I think I'm going to Ecuador. Vera, you know I'm not into politics. They watch me and check up on me as if I was an extremist. I'm the head of this section but I have to show everything to a stuffed shirt of an officer who hasn't a clue. Every time I go for a piss he watches me as if I was going to plant a bomb."

"Mr. Erazo, you're the only person I know that can help me."

"I'm sorry about this, Vera. You'd better go. They're going to haul you in again any moment on any old pretext. I'd advise you to get out of Chile. I'm leaving, and I'm perfectly clean. You have to disappear."

I said good-bye. What was I going to do? I felt very much alone. I would meet good friends in the street, comrades from the party who hadn't been picked up. They'd look at me, barely say hello, and hurry on. They were dodging me. People were jumpy. Who was that, that So-and-so was talking to?... They were scared. I'd been fingered.

* * *

Every Wednesday I went to the police station. One day I was met by a corporal.

"What do you want?"

"I've come to sign," I said timidly.

"Oh! You're a prisoner, eh?"

"Yes."

"What's your name?"

"Vera."

He looked everywhere in the B's and couldn't find me. I said:

"Vera with a V."

He paused in his search and shouted at me, arrogant and furious:

"Who the hell asked you?"

He started again under V and found my card. He gave me a suspicious look and called two policemen from the corridor. He pointed at me:

"This is Vera."

He made an odd gesture.

One of the men said:

"You're Vera, eh?"

I didn't know what kind of game this was. The cop shut the door and went on:

"Good thing you turned up. We were waiting for you."

"Where are the arms?"

What could I say?

"One of your comrades accused you," the corporal said.

He called in three more cops. They caught me under the arms and dragged me out. Out to the courtyard of the station. And I was screaming.

The corporal burst out laughing.

"Cry-baby!"

Then he gave a sharp order:

"Shoot him!"

They put me up against a wall and lined up in front of me with their guns. They fired all around my body and I could feel the chips flying from the adobe wall. I shut my eyes and shit myself for fear. I couldn't believe what was happening. I opened my eyes and there they were, still in front of me with their guns. I was sweating like a horse. They started firing again, and the corporal said over and over:

"Took us for suckers, did you?"

I didn't dare look. I was horrified by the idea of pain. And death. I shouted at them:

"Kill me! Kill me!"

They were shooting again into thin air. Then they came over to me and kicked me into the office. The corporal showed me my card and spoke to me as if what had just happened had never been.

"There, Vera, sign here and keep your nose out of politics, and don't blab this to anybody or we'll kill you for real next time."

I got home with my pants full of shit, and I started to drink. I got drunk in front of the TV, watching some military type in a green suit reading out rules about I don't know what. I shouted sarcastic comments at him and laughed to myself. Carmen and my father watched me in silence. They'd be killed, too. And I'd be tortured, and I'd be killed. We'd all be wiped out.

"I've got to get out of this country. I've had it."

Afterwards I repeated this phrase in my head, so I wouldn't lose it, so there'd be no doubt that it was the only solution. I said aloud:

"Hey, we sell the TV and I go."

"Cool down, Slim. Things will be all right."

My father came and sat beside me. He had trouble talking because he had cancer of the mouth.

"There's a church in Santiago that helps people to get out of the country," he said slowly.

Crazed and desperate, I got up and left. I jumped aboard a train for Santiago. The cars were full of soldiers eating chicken sandwiches and drinking Cokes. I wondered where they got all the money to buy that stuff in the dining car. I was nauseous and shivering. But they didn't check my papers.

The church was downtown. A few soldiers were strolling up and down in groups, keeping an eye out and trying to look casual. I went in through a half-open side door. There were people dispersed all about the nave, some sitting in the pews, others asleep, whole families with their luggage. They had set up school desks and there was a lineup leading to each where you waited to be interviewed. I joined one, and a girl came over to me. I tried to speak so the others couldn't hear, explaining to her that I'd been in prison for a year. That I had run away from my home town. That I wanted out. When she had heard my incoherent story the girl went off to discuss it with a lawyer. She came back with him and I showed him the documents saying I was out on conditional release.

"And what do you want?" he asked, with obvious distaste.

"I want to go to Argentina."

"But things there are just as bad as here, if not worse. Look, if you really want to leave, you should go to Australia or Canada. And here, by the way, is a little nun who can help you."

The lawyer moved off. A pale woman in grey took down my details and gave me a form requesting emigration.

"Fill this out and leave it at the Canadian Embassy."

I started off, walking toward the embassy. What did I know about Canada? They spoke English there. I arrived at Ahumada Street. Soldiers were standing guard on the sidewalk. The embassy was on the second floor. I took the elevator and went up. The office was packed with people applying. A secretary was handing out slips of paper. I went to her and told her about the form I had filled out. She looked at me, surprised, then, realizing where I had come from, answered:

"Give it to me and send the copy by mail."

So I went back to Rancagua. I worked here and there, as day labourer in the construction business, or unloading sacks of potatoes, or delivering merchandise. Or painting houses. Nothing much doing. I took out a passport, got my tax papers and my certificate of good behaviour. Finally I was called in for an interview at the embassy. Then for another interview, and another. The last time, an official asked me several times why I had been arrested. And whether I had a criminal record. And what party I belonged to. And whether I intended to act against the Chilean government once I got to Canada. And what I was going to work at there. I said, doing whatever I could get. I didn't mind. Suddenly the man said:

"Look, Mr. Vera, everything's in order. You have enough points." And he handed me the plane ticket. "I'm giving you the ticket now, but there's just one catch. You're confined to Rancagua. We can't do anything about that. You have to ask permission from the military government."

That was a blow. I wanted to say something, but he went on:

"Why don't you go to C.I.N.E., it's a European emigration committee. I'll give you an introduction with the whole story."

He typed something and gave me the paper. The committee was in an old building. I asked to see the person in charge. It turned out to be a German, smiling and sporty-looking. I showed him my introduction, and told him my problem. He laughed contemptuously when I mentioned the military, and said:

"Go and ask permission from the interrogation centre. Perhaps they can...."

Back to Rancagua again. I followed instructions like a robot. I got dressed up in a dark suit and white shirt and slicked my hair down with Brilliantine. Then went to the interrogation centre. The new prosecutor was trying to be efficient, and saw people at once. There was no lineup. I went straight inside. He was young and well dressed, smelled of shaving lotion and wore a polite smile.

He closed the door behind me and offered me a chair.

"Please sit down. Would you care for a coffee?"

He was so friendly, I felt I could actually tell him why I had come. I began, but my voice sounded strained:

"Well, the fact is... I'm a former prisoner of war."

He stood up, his friendly manner giving way to an inexplicable fury.

"A political prisoner, are you? A Marxist, eh?"

The sudden change disconcerted me. I was unable to say anything but:

"Yes, yes..."

"Well! What had you been up to?" His voice was like a hammer.

"I... I don't know."

"What do you mean, you don't know, you bastard? I suppose you're lily-white, are you?"

He paused, saw my dismay, and went on:

"And what is it you're after?"

I didn't want to answer. With his insulting, brutal manner, I wanted to smash his teeth in, take him down a peg, spoil him, spit on him. My voice came out almost inaudible, painfully slow:

"Sir, what I wanted was permission to leave the country."

"Leave the country!" He was impressed. "And where would you go, pray?"

"To Canada," I replied meekly.

"I'd like to know how Canada can open its doors to this kind of people, a country so prosperous, so rich, so free, a country so... so fine as Canada."

"It's not... I'll go to work there, you know."

"What will you be able to do in Canada? You're just an ignorant working man. That's a highly industrialized country. Decent people, strong people. Now if I were to go there... But you? I can't imagine it."

He gave a hysterical laugh and exclaimed:

"Forget about your permission. If you skip out, you won't leave this building alive next time."

I was paralyzed and tense. I didn't dare make a move.

"Now get out, do you hear me?"

He opened the door and spoke to the guard with the machine gun in the hall:

"We should shoot them all while they're here. Those people are going to get together outside the country and wipe us out."

* * *

I took the Santiago train, tired and feeling as if I'd been trying all my life to leave the country. It was just three days until my flight left. I went again to see the German. He always sounded convincing. This time he sent me to the Dina, a military security organization with its offices in the former parliament building. The gardens of that defunct institution were full of weeping women. Inside, an unbelievable crowd of people lining up to ask about those who had disappeared. Of course they wept when there was no news. I got my courage together and went inside. An officer stationed in the doorway was saying:

"That's it, now, everybody out, no more today, and tomorrow's a day off for the army."

I pushed my way over to him:

"Lieutenant, I have to leave in three days and I need a permit from the Dina."

I showed him my papers where it said "Free" and "stay of proceedings." The officer stared at my clothing, saw it was clean and that I had shaved. He asked:

"Just cut your beard, did you?"

"I never had a beard," I answered, astounded.

"Over this way, then," he said curtly.

He took my papers and went toward the offices. Maybe they'd keep me here. What a crazy idea of that German's, to go get permission from the military! This was a dictatorship! Why couldn't I get that into my head? No law. No order. No morality. Authorization my ass. Another officer stuck his head out of an office and shouted:

"Vera!"

I was shaking in my boots.

"Here!"

"It seems you want to take a trip."

"Yes!"

He looked me up and down, but in a friendly way.

"Well, you know, you don't need any papers to leave the country. There's been a stay of proceedings. That means you're cleared of all guilt. And you were never arrested."

"I just thought I'd feel better if I had a paper..."

"All right, just as you like."

They typed up a document. And I left. The women were still weeping in the gardens for those who had disappeared.

* * *

"Vera! Hey, Vera!"

I cried out, terrified. Somebody was shaking me. I heard a man's voice say: "Get up, it's six thirty!"

I opened my eyes and saw Ljubetic over in the corner of the room making coffee. The room was empty, except for two mattresses on the floor, donated by the solidarity committee.

"What the hell was wrong with you?" asked Ljubetic.

"I dreamed I was back in Chile and couldn't get out."

I washed and dressed and walked to St. Lawrence Boulevard. All the stores were closed. I took the 55 bus. It was empty. A few people got on as we climbed the slope. I got a wave from two Haitians who work in the same factory I do, and I waved back. Later I saw the row of factories through the bus window and I thought, half of Canada was made up of types like me, people who had to leave their countries to get a lousy job in a factory.

* * *

NOTE ON THE AUTHOR

Born in Santiago, Chile in 1945, Marilù Mallet has lived in Canada since 1973. The five stories in this collection were first published in French as *Les Compagnons de l'horloge-pointeuse* in 1981 by Éditions Québec-Amérique. Known also as a filmmaker, Mallet's films have received critical acclaim in Canada and abroad. Most recently her film 'Journal Inachevé' won the *Prix spécial du jury* at the Biarritz Film Festival and the *Prix de la critique québécoise*. With another collection of short stories now in translation the author is currently working on a novel and a new film.

NOTE ON THE TRANSLATOR

Alan Brown began translating in 1963 while living in Europe; two books by Cendrars and one by Giono, for a British publisher. Since returning to Canada he has translated some twenty-five books by Québecois writers including *The Antiphonary* by Hubert Aquin which was awarded the Canada Council Translation Prize in 1974.

ALSO PUBLISHED BY VÉHICULE PRESS

FICTION

The Bequest & Other Stories by Jerry Wexler

POETRY

Veiled Countries/Lives by Marie-Claire Blais
Translated by Michael Harris (A Signal Edition)

A Nun's Diary by Anne McLean (A Signal Edition)

Cavalier in a Roundhead School by Errol MacDonald
(A Signal Edition)

Anyone Skating on That Middle Ground by Robyn Sarah

Blind Painting by Robert Melançon
Translated by Philip Stratford (A Signal Edition)

Small Horses & Intimate Beasts by Michael Garneau
Translated by Robert McGee (A Signal Edition)

ON WRITERS AND WRITING

Spider Blues: Essays on Michael Ondaatje
edited by Sam Solecki

The Montreal Story Tellers: Memoirs, Photographs, Critical Essays
edited by J.R. (Tim) Struthers

Ideas for Poetry by Louis Dudek